Keyfacts

GCSE PASSBOOK

SCIENCE

Bob McDuell

First published 1990

Reprinted 1991

Illustrations: Tek Art Ltd.

Text: © Bob McDuell 1990, 1991

© BPP (Letts Educational) Ltd
Aldine House, Aldine Place
142-144 Uxbridge Road
London
W12 8AW

British Library Cataloguing in Publication Data
McDuell, G. R. (Godfrey Robert) *1944 –*
 Science.
 1. Science
 I. Title
 500
ISBN 1 85758 161 X

Printed and bound in Great Britain by
WM Print Ltd, Frederick Street, Walsall, West Midlands WS2 9NE. (0922) 643008

Moby Lawrenson.

Contents

		Page
Preface		4
Introduction and guide to using this book		5
Hints on how to approach Science examinations		6
1	Energy and fuels	7
2	Electricity	26
3	Magnetism	39
4	Waves	51
5	Force and motion	59
6	Feedback and control	68
7	The human body	78
8	Reproduction and inheritance	89
9	Ecology	96
10	Solar system, rocks and weather	104
11	Matter and particles	112
12	The Periodic Table	133
13	Chemical reactions	143
14	Acids, alkalis and salts	156
15	Metals and polymers	166
Answers to revision questions		183
Final examination advice		192

Preface

This Passbook is one of a series of Letts Keyfacts Passbooks designed to provide a concise revision course for GCSE. This book is designed to cover the double science criteria used as the basis of Science syllabuses for:

- University of London Examinations and Assessment Council (ULEAC)
- Midland Examining Group (MEG)
- Northern Examining Association (NEA)
- Northern Ireland Schools Examinations and Assessment Council (NISEAC)
- Scottish Examinations Board (SEB)
- Southern Examining Group (SEG)
- Welsh Joint Education Committee (WJEC).

The basic content of the book is divided into 15 sections. In each section there is a clear statement of aims, a concise treatment of the topic, a summary and practice questions of the type used on GCSE papers. Many of these questions involve using information rather than just recall of knowledge.

The book also gives you advice on planning revision and actually taking the examinations. In some cases GCSE Science courses involve regular modular tests taken throughout the course. This book is useful then as a course companion to help you as you go through the course.

I should like to thank my editor and the staff at Letts Educational for all their help during the preparation of this book. I would also like to thank my wife, Judy, and my sons Robin and Timothy for their help and support.

All Science courses leading to GCSE must contain a certain content called the **core**. The core must make up at least 60 per cent of any syllabus. This book is designed to help you to master this core as this is the key to success.

The book is divided into 15 chapters. You are advised to work through all of the chapters. After you have read through a chapter go through it again with a highlighter pen and mark parts that you think are particularly important. Key statements are marked in the margin. When you have been through the chapter, write out your own summary using the highlighted sections to help you. Each summary should be no longer than one sheet of A4 paper. Compare your summaries with those printed at the end of each chapter. Keep these summaries as they will be useful for final revision. Attempt the questions at the end of each chapter and check your answers with the answers at the back of the book.

Grade your understanding of each chapter on a scale:

A you understand the chapter very well;

B you understand the chapter but are not confident about it;

C you find the chapter difficult.

When you have been through all of the chapters go back and look again at chapters you graded **C** and then those you graded **B**.

In the final days of revision go back and re-read your summaries. Try and write out the summaries from memory.

Hints on how to approach Science examinations

A planned revision programme is essential if you are going to achieve your best results in GCSE.

1 Start your revision early
The earlier you start the better. However, it is never too late to start.

2 Find a good place and time to revise
Try to find a quiet place to revise. Many students believe they can revise watching television or listening to records or the radio, but this is not recommended. Try to revise at a regular time each day. Good revising should become a habit! Research has shown that about 30 minutes of intensive revision followed by a **short** break is suitable for most people.

3 Plan your revision
It is important to set yourself targets and draw up a revision timetable. This timetable should include time for you to relax, exercise and enjoy yourself. Do not just pick up this Passbook or your notes and start reading. Too often students doing this know the first sections well, because they have read them a number of times, but do not know the later chapters.

Aim to study one chapter each day. In addition to reading your Passbook, you should look at the same section in your notes or other books. Also, you should look for further questions to try on the same topic.

4 Find out exactly what is required
Ask your teacher for details of the syllabus so you know when you are taking examinations and what these examinations will consist of. Your teacher will also tell you about the coursework assessment that you will have to do. If you want help with your coursework you should buy **Letts Science Coursework Companion**. Remember that coursework is important as these marks are 'already in the bag' before your start taking the examination.

5 Try to assess what you know
As was explained earlier, extra time should be spent on the chapters you do not fully understand. There is a tendency to leave out difficult bits or bits you do not understand. All of the contents of the Passbook should be understood as they can all come up in examinations.

Aims of the chapter

After reading this chapter you should:

1 Know that energy makes things happen and is measured in units of **joules**.

2 Be able to distinguish various forms of energy – light, nuclear, chemical, heat, electrical, mechanical and sound.

3 Be able to distinguish between two forms of mechanical energy – kinetic and potential.

4 Know that energy can be transferred from one form to another and be able to give examples of energy changes in everyday life.

5 Be able to distinguish between energy, work and power.

6 Be able to describe three methods of heat transfer – conduction, convection and radiation.

7 Be able to describe simple experiments to demonstrate conduction, convection and radiation.

8 Know where heat is lost from a house and how different methods of insulation help to reduce heat loss.

9 Be able to describe the properties of a good fuel and make decisions about most suitable fuels.

10 Be able to explain the terms **fossil fuel** and **renewable fuel**.

11 Be able to describe problems such as the **greenhouse effect**, caused by burning fossil fuels.

12 Be able to describe alternative sources of energy.

Energy

Energy makes things happen. It can exist in different forms and can be converted from one form to another. It can be stored in fuels and other chemicals.

Energy is measured with units called **joules** (J), named after the famous scientist James Prescott Joule (1818–1889). He lived in Manchester and carried out many energy experiments.

Different forms of energy

Energy can exist in seven different forms. These are summarized in Fig. 1. You can remember them if you remember the name (albeit rather strange!)

L.N. CHEMS

– light, nuclear, chemical, heat, electrical, mechanical and sound.

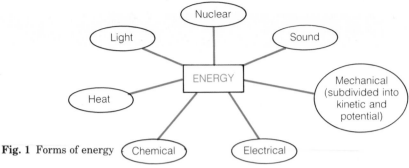

Fig. 1 Forms of energy

We shall look at the different forms of energy and look at examples where energy is converted from one form to another.

Light energy

Light is a form of energy. Light will make plants grow and power solar cells. Light will cause objects to warm up. Apart from visible light, there are other forms of **electromagnetic radiation**. These include X-rays, ultra-violet and infra-red radiation.

Nuclear energy

Elements such as uranium are radioactive (pp. 127-9). This means that the nuclei of the atoms split up and emit very large amounts of energy, much of it in the form of heat. In a nuclear power station this energy is used to produce steam to drive turbines.

Chemical energy

Chemicals can be regarded as **stores of energy**. This energy can be released when required. For example, coal, oil and gas are examples of chemicals which burn and produce heat energy.

A battery for your torch contains chemicals. When the chemicals are used up the battery stops working.

Heat energy

Heat is a form of energy. We can see that heat can make things happen. When ice is heated it will melt. On further heating the water will boil. When a piece of metal is heated it will expand. If it is heated more strongly it will glow and light will be emitted.

All matter contains energy and when chemical changes occur there is usually an energy change (pp. 147-8).

Electrical energy

Electrical energy is a very convenient form of energy because it can easily be converted into other forms. Many appliances are powered by electricity.

Electricity cannot be stored. However, it is possible to store energy in chemicals ready for use when required.

The quantity of energy passing through a wire depends upon the **current** in amperes, the **potential difference** in volts and the **time** in seconds. Increase any of these and the total energy will increase.

Energy (in J) = Current (in A) × Potential difference (in V) × Time (in s)

$$E = IVt$$

Example Calculate the energy used when a torch containing a 9 V battery and using a current of 0.25 A is used for 5 minutes. Using the above equation.

$I = 0.25$ A

$V = 9$ V

$t = 5$ minutes $= 5 \times 60 = 300$ s

$E = 0.25 \times 9 \times 300$ J

$\quad = 675$ J

Mechanical energy

Mechanical energy can be divided into **kinetic energy** (KE) and **potential energy** (PE).

The stretched elastic in a catapult contains stored energy. This stored energy is called potential energy. When the elastic is released, the stored energy is released.

An object resting on the ground possesses no energy. When the object is held in the air it has potential energy: the potential to be pulled down by gravity. When the object is dropped the potential energy is released.

Water in the reservoir in Fig. 2 possesses potential energy. When it is allowed to fall the energy is released and turns a turbine which in turn generates electricity.

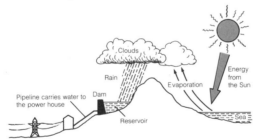

Fig. 2 Energy from the reservoir

Any object which is moving has some kinetic energy. The kinetic energy possessed by an object depends upon the mass of the object (in kg) and the velocity (in m/s).

Kinetic energy (in J) = ½ × mass × velocity^2

$$KE = \tfrac{1}{2}mv^2$$

Example Calculate the kinetic energy possessed by an object weighing 100 kg, moving with velocity of 20 m/s.

$KE = \tfrac{1}{2} \times 100$ kg $\times 20$ m/s $\times 20$ m/s

$\quad = 20\ 000$ J or 20 kJ

A joule is a very small amount of energy. When you walk upstairs you use 1000 J. Often amounts of energy are given in units of kilojoules (kJ).

1000 J = 1 kJ

Very large amounts of energy may be given in units of megajoules (MJ).

1 000 000 J = 1 MJ

Sound energy

Sound is a form of energy. Sound energy is passed through particles. Unlike light energy, sound energy cannot be passed through an empty space.

Energy changes

There are many examples where energy changes from one form to another. The following examples illustrate some changes.

1 *Television*
A television converts electrical energy into light energy, sound energy and heat energy.

2 *Microphone*
A microphone converts sound into electrical energy.

3 *Atomic bomb*
An atomic bomb converts nuclear energy into heat energy, light energy and sound energy.

4 *Car engine*
A car engine converts chemical energy (stored in the fuel) into mechanical energy, heat energy and sound energy. In many cases more than one form of energy is produced. Often, however, one form of energy is more important. The information can be shown in an **energy arrow** (see Fig. 3). Other examples of energy changes are included in the Revision Questions at the end of this chapter.

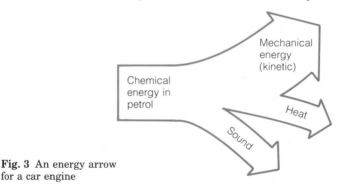

Fig. 3 An energy arrow for a car engine

The conservation of energy

The work of Joule around 1850 was revolutionary and difficult for other scientists to accept. He showed that when energy is converted from one form to another, none is lost and none is gained. This is embodied in the Principle of Conservation of Energy.

Energy cannot be created or destroyed. It can be changed from one form to another.

However, some energy conversions appear to lose energy. For example, not all of the chemical energy in the petrol of a car is converted into mechanical energy. We have seen already in Fig. 3 that some energy is converted into other forms which do not help to move the car. The sum of all the different forms of energy produced must equal the amount of energy stored in the fuel.

Energy, work and power

There is confusion in Science between the terms energy, work and power.
Work is energy being used up. It can be calculated from the force (in newtons) and distance moved (in metres).

Work done (in J) = Force (in N) × Distance moved (in m)

Example A box requires a force of 50 N to move it. Find the work done in moving the box 10 m.

Work done = 50 × 10 J
= 500 J

Power is the rate of doing work.

$$\text{Power} = \frac{\text{Work done (in J)}}{\text{Time taken (in s)}}$$

NB Work and energy are not connected with time but power is connected with time.

Power is measured in watts (W).

1 watt (1 W) = 1 joule of work done in one second

Example Calculate the work done when a load weighing 1000 N is lifted through a height of 10 m. Then calculate the power when the lifting is completed in 10 s.

Work done = Force × Distance moved
= 1000 N × 10 m
= 10 000 J

$$\begin{aligned} \text{Power} &= \frac{\text{Work done}}{\text{Time taken}} \\ &= \frac{10\ 000\ \text{J}}{10\ \text{s}} \\ &= 1000\ \text{W or 1 kW} \end{aligned}$$

Remember A 1 kW electric fire uses 1000 J each second.

Transfer of heat energy

K There are three methods of transferring heat energy: convection, conduction and radiation.

Convection

Convection can take place in a material which is a **fluid** (i.e. liquid or gas). The heat energy is transferred by movement of particles. The particles take the energy from place to place. The movement of particles is called a **convection current**.

Fig. 4 shows a simple experiment to demonstrate convection in a liquid. A crystal of potassium manganate(VII) (sometimes called potassium permanganate) is added to the water. When the beaker is heated, as shown in the diagram, convection currents are set up. The coloured warmer water, which is less dense, rises and the denser cold water moves in to replace it.

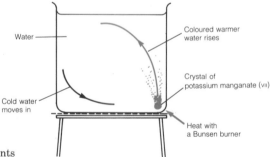

Water

Cold water moves in

Coloured warmer water rises

Crystal of potassium manganate (VII)

Heat with a Bunsen burner

Fig. 4 Convection currents

A heating system in a large room can set up similar convection currents. The heated air rises and cold air falls to replace it. As a result our feet can be very cold even though the room is well heated.

Convection currents are also responsible for sea breezes. During the day the land heats up more quickly than the sea. The hot air rises above the land and cool air comes in from the sea to replace it. The result is a breeze blowing onshore from the sea (Fig. 5).

At night the situation is reversed. Now the land cools more quickly than the sea. Convection currents rise from the sea and cool air from the land blows offshore to replace it. The effect is a breeze from land to sea (Fig. 6).

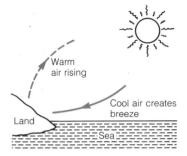

Fig. 5 Onshore sea breezes

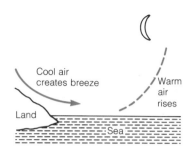

Fig. 6 Offshore sea breezes

Conduction

Conduction is the transfer of heat energy along a piece of material. The most important examples of conduction occur in solids, where convection is impossible. Conduction can take place in fluids.

The heat energy is passed from one particle to the next. The particles do not have to change their positions in order to pass on the energy. This is one big difference between conduction and convection.

A substance which passes on heat energy well is called a **good conductor**. Metals are very good conductors of heat. A substance which is a very poor conductor of heat is called an **insulator**.

Fig. 7 shows an experiment to find out which of five metals is the best conductor of heat. One end of each metal rod is coated with wax and the other end of each rod is heated in the same hot water bath. (This ensures the metal rods are all heated by the same amount.) The best conductor of heat will be the metal where the wax first starts to drip.

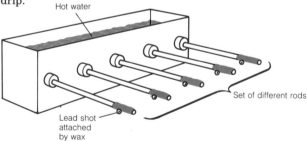

Fig. 7 Testing heat conductors

Radiation

The energy coming to the Earth from the Sun cannot come by convection or conduction, which both require particles to transfer the heat energy. Between the Earth and the Sun is empty space.

The energy in this case is transferred by radiation. There are many different kinds of radiation but when we are considering heating effects it is called **infra-red radiation**. The energy is given out by a **source**. In the case we are considering, this is the Sun. The Sun radiates energy because it is very hot and this energy is felt directly on the Earth.

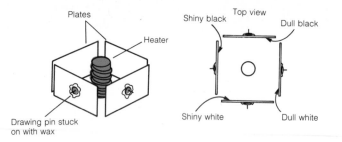

Fig. 8 Testing how well surfaces absorb heat

In a similar way if you hold your hand a small distance away from an electric fire your hand will feel warm. The fire radiates heat directly in all directions and you feel the warmth on your hand.

Radiation is direct and travels in straight lines. It can travel through empty space.

The **absorbing** and **emitting** power of different surfaces can vary. Fig. 8 shows an experiment to compare how well four surfaces absorb radiation from a source, in this case a small electric heater. On the back of each sheet there is a drawing pin fixed to the sheet with wax. The first drawing pin which will fall off its sheet will be the one attached to the sheet which absorbs heat best.

The results obtained show that:
(a) Dark, dull surfaces are the best absorbers of heat energy.
(b) Bright, shiny surfaces are the worst absorbers.

When considering the emission of radiation it is found that:
(a) Dark, dull surfaces are the best emitters of radiation.
(b) Bright, shiny surfaces are the worst emitters.

Heat losses in the home

In winter, up to a third of the energy used in Great Britain is used to heat homes. Much of this energy is lost due to inadequate insulation. Fig. 9 summarizes how the heat energy is lost in a typical home.

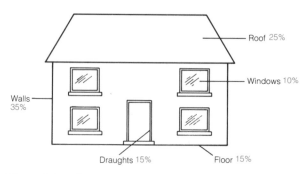

Fig. 9 Heat losses from a house

There is much that can be done to reduce heat losses from a home and therefore reduce fuel costs.

1 Loft insulation
Much of the heat loss through the roof can be saved by insulation with mineral wool laid between the joists. Trapped between the fibres of the wood is air and this makes the material a good **insulator**. This layer of insulation prevents heat loss by conduction. Modern standards of insulation recommend a thickness of 15 cm.

2 Sealing drafts
Draft excluding strips prevent currents of cold air from entering and setting up convection currents. It is, however, essential that there is adequate ventilation for open fires and gas fires if they are to burn safely without a build-up of the poisonous fumes they produce.

3 Double glazing
Some of the heat can be loss through the windows although you will notice this is a relatively small amount. This loss of energy can be reduced by fitting double glazing. This is formed from two panes of glass with air trapped between them (Fig. 10). The two panes of glass and the trapped air act as a good insulator and prevent heat escaping. Double glazing can be expensive. It does, however, reduce condensation and helps soundproof the house.

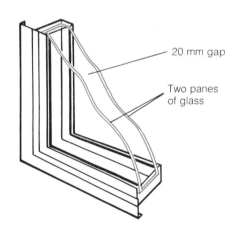

20 mm gap

Two panes of glass

Fig. 10 Double glazing

4 Cavity wall insulation
In most houses the outside walls are made up of two walls with a small gap or cavity between them. Air in this cavity can move about and convection currents can be set up. If the cavity is filled with polystyrene beads or foam, which are good insulators, these currents cannot be set up. Much less heat energy is then lost through the walls.

5 *Carpets and underlay*

Much of the heat loss through the floor can be prevented by fitting thick carpets and underlay. Both trap air and produce good insulation. This prevents conduction through the floor.

Comparing fuels

Fig. 11 shows a simple experiment to compare the energy produced when two fuels are burnt. The first fuel is methylated spirit (in a spirit lamp) and the second is a piece of fire lighter. In each case the amount of fuel used can be measured by weighing before and after the experiment. The same mass (or volume) of water is used in each case. Table 1 gives some results for two fuels labelled A and B.

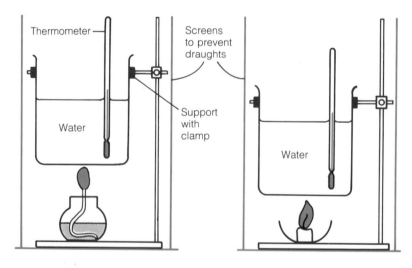

Fig. 11 Comparing fuels

	Fuel A	**Fuel B**
Mass of water	100 g	100g
Mass of fuel used	0.5 g	1.0 g
Temperature before	20 °C	20 °C
Temperature after	43 °C	35 °C
Cost of fuel (p per 100 g)	5	1

Table 1

Looking at these results you should be able to conclude that:
(a) fuel A produces more energy per gram burned than fuel B. (There was a bigger temperature rise even though only half the quantity was burnt.)
(b) fuel B is more economical.

When selecting the best fuel for a particular purpose price is an obvious consideration. However, there are other things to consider. These include:
(a) How readily available is it?
(b) How cleanly does it burn? Does it produce unpleasant fumes?
(c) Is it a solid, liquid or a gas? How is it delivered and stored?
(d) How easy is it to set alight?

Fossil fuels

Some fuels, such as coal, petroleum and natural gas, are **fossil fuels**. Coal was produced by the action of heat and pressure on trees and plants over millions of years. The trees and plants obtained their energy from the Sun and the Sun is the original source of all our energy. Petroleum and natural gas were produced by the action of heat and pressure on tiny sea creatures over million of years.

Fossil fuels took millions of years to produce and we are using them up rapidly. The amounts in the Earth are limited and will eventually be used up. It is important, therefore, to find alternative energy sources and to use existing energy sources carefully.

Wood is a **renewable fuel**. Every year fresh supplies can be grown and, with sensible use, should never run out. However, due to greed and necessity in some parts of the world, more timber is being felled than is being grown.

In Brazil, ethanol (alcohol) is being produced by fermenation of sugar. Every year new sugar cane is grown and fresh stocks of ethanol can be produced. Ethanol is another renewable fuel.

When fossil fuels burn they produce carbon dioxide. The increased use of fossil fuels, and the felling of large areas of forest, is increasing the percentage of carbon dioxide in the atmosphere. Scientists are already recognizing effects which could be serious in the future.

Radiation passes through the Earth's atmosphere and heats up the Earth. The heated Earth starts to radiate energy but this energy has a relatively short wavelength. This radiation does not pass through the carbon dioxide in the atmosphere and escape. The temperature of the Earth rises and this can alter the climate of the Earth. It is predicted that the ice caps at the poles could partially melt, causing sea levels to rise and land to be submerged. In Great Britain the summers could become hotter and drier and the winters colder and wetter. These changes could affect the way we live on the planet. This effect is called the **greenhouse effect** (Fig. 12).

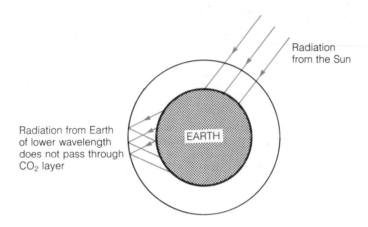

Fig. 12 The greenhouse effect

Alternative forms of energy

As deposits of fossil fuels become more expensive to mine and start to run out – and also to halt the effects of global warming – we should start to look at alternative sources of energy.

Solar energy

More energy arrives at the Earth's surface in an hour than is used by the world in a whole year. Even in Britain, lying in the Northern Hemisphere, with its cold winters and the Sun being hidden by heavy cloud, the total solar energy received each year is 80 times our present energy demand.

At present we do not use solar energy very well. Some houses, hotels and factories have solar panels fitted on the roof (Fig. 13). These panels are painted dull black to make them good absorbers of radiant energy. The solar-heated water in the panels is circulated and used to preheat water entering a hot water tank. Less energy is then used to heat the water.

Solar cells can be used to convert radiation directly into electricity. Calculators, watches etc. can be powered in this way. In developing countries this kind of technology can be used to produce electricity to pump water etc.

A more revolutionary method involves locating the solar cells in orbit around the Earth. They can be more effective there. The radiation is converted into microwave energy which is then transmitted to a ground station where it is converted into electricity (Fig. 14).

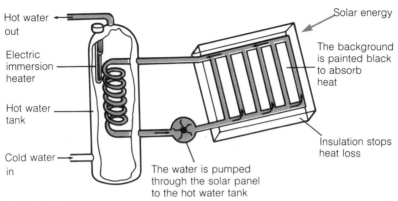

Fig. 13 Solar panels

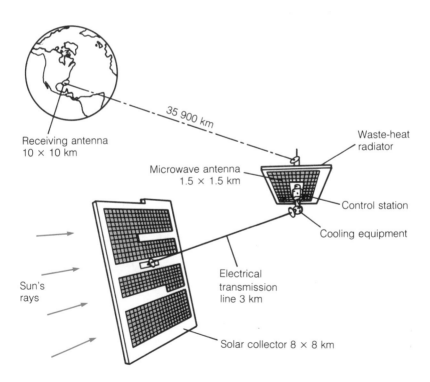

Fig. 14 Orbiting solar cells

Wind energy

We have used wind energy in the past for windmills. However, with new technology it is possible to collect energy from the wind more effectively and convert it into electricity.

Fig. 15 shows a modern wind turbine. A whole series of these could produce up to 20 per cent of the electricity needed in Britain.

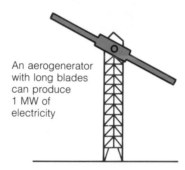

An aerogenerator with long blades can produce 1 MW of electricity

Fig. 15 A modern wind turbine

Hydroelectric energy

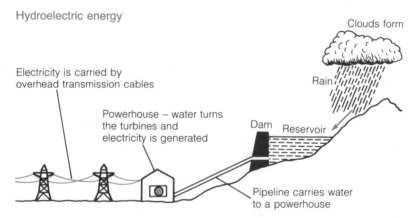

Clouds form

Electricity is carried by overhead transmission cables

Rain

Powerhouse – water turns the turbines and electricity is generated

Dam   Reservoir

Pipeline carries water to a powerhouse

Fig. 16 Hydroelectric energy

Fig. 16 shows how a hydroelectric power station operates. Electricity is generated by water falling from the reservoir. Its potential energy is converted into kinetic energy which is used to turn a turbine which, in turn, generates electricity.

Fig. 17 shows where hydroelectric power stations are built. You will notice that these are mainly in Scotland, Wales and the West Country of England. All these areas are hilly, so suitable reservoirs can be

built. The West of England, Scotland and Wales also have higher
rainfall than other parts of Britain.

Fig. 17 Hydroelectric power stations in Britain

Tidal energy

In a dam in the estuary of the River Rance in France, there is a power
station which generates electricity using tidal power. The working of
the power station is shown in Fig. 18. A similar dam across the Severn
estuary could produce 20 per cent of the electricity needed in Britain.

Wave energy

The movement of ocean waves could be harnessed to produce energy.
Experiments have been carried out by using large rafts which float up
and down with the waves. This rocking movement can be converted
into electricity.

Geothermal energy

This is not a renewable source of energy. It relies on the fact that the
rocks beneath the Earth's surface are much hotter than surface rocks.
Countries such as France, Hungary, Japan and New Zealand rely on
geothermal energy. Water is pumped below ground and then pumped

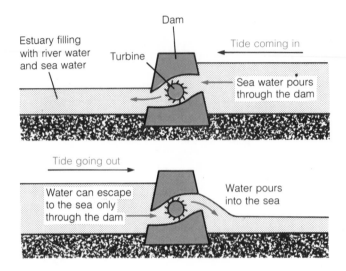

Fig. 18 The Rance dam

again to the surface. The water is thus preheated before being used in the usual generating methods.

Summary

Energy makes things happen and is measured in joules (J). It exists as light, nuclear, chemical, heat, electrical, mechanical and sound energy. Nuclear energy involves the breakdown of radioactive atoms such as uranium. Very large amounts of energy are given out.

Chemicals can be regarded as **stores of energy**, which can be released when required. Electrical energy is a very convenient form of energy because it can easily be converted into other forms. Electricity cannot be stored. However, it is possible to store energy in chemicals ready for use when required.

The quantity of energy passing through a wire can be found using the formula:

$E = IVt$

where E is the energy (in J), I is the current (in A), V is the potential difference (in V) and t is the time (in s).

Mechanical energy can be divided into **kinetic energy** (KE) and **potential energy** (PE). Stored energy is called potential energy. Any object which is moving has some kinetic energy. The kinetic energy

possessed by an object is given by the formula:
$KE = \frac{1}{2}mv^2$
where KE is the kinetic energy (in J), m is the mass (in kg) and v is the velocity (in m/s).

Sound energy is passed through **particles**. Unlike light energy, sound energy cannot be passed through an empty space.

There are many examples where energy **changes** from one form to another. When this takes place energy cannot be created or destroyed. Work is energy being used up. It can be calculated by multiplying the force (in N) by the distance moved (in m).

Power is the rate of doing work and the units are watts (W).

$$\text{Power} = \frac{\text{Work done (in J)}}{\text{Time taken (in s)}}$$

1 watt (1 W) = 1 joule of work done in one second

There are three methods of transferring heat energy: convection, conduction and radiation. Dark, dull surfaces are the best absorbers of heat energy. Bright, shiny surfaces are the worst absorbers. Dark, dull surfaces are the best emitters of radiation and bright, shiny surfaces are the worst emitters.

There is considerable **heat loss** from the home. Much of this heat could be saved with good **insulation** such as loft insulation, cavity wall insulation etc.

Some fuels, such as coal, petroleum and natural gas are **fossil fuels**. The amounts in the Earth are limited and will eventually be used up. Renewable fuels such as wood and ethanol can be replaced by new supplies. Burning fossil fuels can lead to problems such as the greenhouse effect. There are possible alternative sources of energy. These include solar energy, wind energy, hydroelectric energy, tidal energy, wave energy and geothermal energy.

Revision questions

1 For each of the following, state the energy change which takes place.
Example A microphone converts **sound energy** into **electrical energy**.
(a) A bicycle dynamo converts .... into ....
(b) The brake blocks on a bicycle, when the brakes are applied, convert .... into ....
(c) A human body converts .... into ....
(d) A light bulb converts .... into ....
(e) A piece of wood, when it burns, converts .... into ....

2 For each of the diagrams in Fig. 19, state whether the method of heat transfer is convection, conduction or radiation.

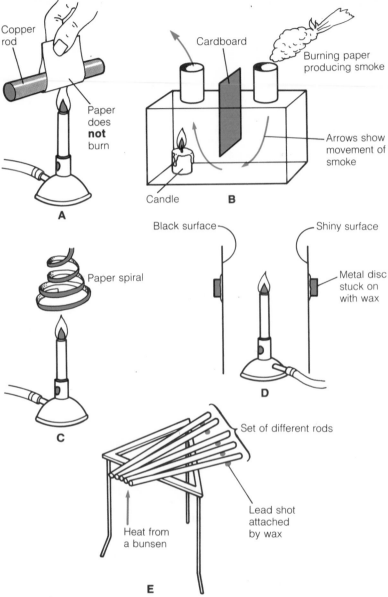

Fig. 19 Methods of heat transfer

3 Fig. 20 shows an experiment. In this experiment all three states of water can be seen – ice, water and steam. What can you conclude about water from this experiment?

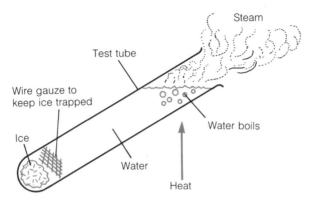

Fig. 20 An experiment

4 Fig. 21 shows the quantity of energy produced when 1 kg of several different fuels is burnt.
(a) Complete the diagram by adding the information for coal. Coal produces 29 MJ per kg.
(b) Which fuel produces the largest amount of energy per kg?

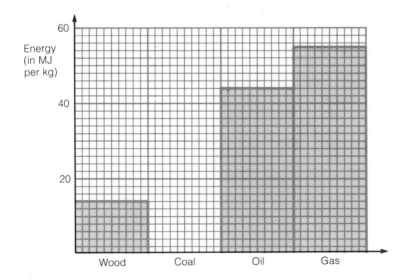

Fig. 21 Energy produced by different fuels

2 Electricity

Aims of the chapter

After reading this chapter you should:
1 Be able to distinguish between conductors of electricity and insulators.
2 Know that electricity flows in a complete circuit.
3 Be able to distinguish between current, potential difference and resistance.
4 Be able to distinguish between series and parallel circuits.
5 Know the common syllabus used in circuit diagrams and be able to draw simple circuit diagrams from information given.
6 Be able to recall the effects of an electric current – magnetic effect, heating effect and chemical effect.
7 Be able to demonstrate a practical knowledge of the supply and distribution of electricity.
8 Be able to explain the principles of a ring main circuit used in a home.
9 Be able to explain the wiring of a three pin plug.
10 Be able to explain the reason for earthing in household circuits.
11 Be able to choose appropriate fuses for household appliances.
12 Be able to calculate the cost of electricity.

Electrical circuits

An electric current is a flow of charged particles, called **electrons**, around a circuit from the negatively charged terminal to the positively charged terminal of the electricity supply. The direction of current flow is shown on a circuit diagram by an arrow.

The current is detected by the lighting of a bulb. The larger the electric current the brighter the bulb grows. The current can be **measured** using an **ammeter** in the circuit. The current is measured in amps (A).

The circuit must be made of materials which are good **electrical conductors**, e.g. metals or carbon (p. 167), which allow current to pass through easily. Wires are covered with plastic or rubber which do not let electricity to pass through. These substances are called **insulators**.

An energy supply is required to push the electrons around the circuit. This can be supplied by a battery, a transformer or a mains supply. The driving force which makes the electric current flow around the circuit is known as the **potential difference** (pd). The potential difference between two points in a circuit is measured on a **voltmeter**. The units for measuring pd are volts (V).

The term **resistance** is used to describe anything which opposes the flow of electricity. A large resistance will allow less electricity to flow around the circuit. The units of resistance are ohms (Ω).

For some experiments a **rheostat** or variable resistance may be used. This will enable the resistance to be altered so that the current flowing in the circuit can be altered.

Drawing circuit diagrams

When we draw a diagramatic representation of an electrical circuit we use certain agreed symbols in the **circuit diagrams**. The common symbols are shown in Fig. 1.

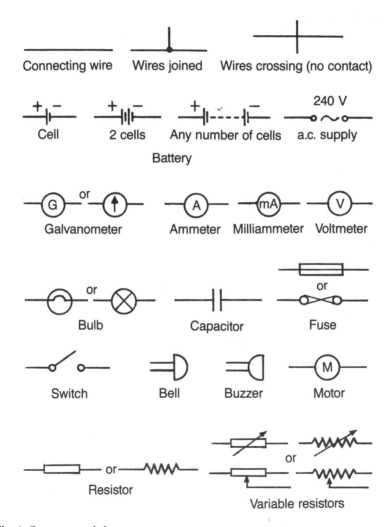

Fig. 1 Common symbols

Fig. 2 shows a simple electrical circuit used to find the potential difference across a bulb. Fig. 3 shows the circuit diagram for the same experiment. Notice that the circuit diagram does not look like the actual diagram but is very much simplified. When you draw a circuit diagram check carefully, but following round the circuit with your finger, that it is a complete circuit.

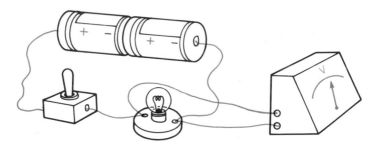

Fig. 2 A simple electrical circuit

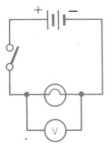

Fig. 3 The circuit diagram

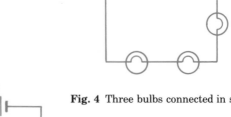

Fig. 4 Three bulbs connected in series

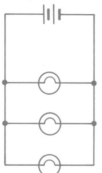

Fig. 5 Three bulbs connected in parallel

Series and parallel circuits

In Fig. 2 the bulb will act as a resistance or resistor. When you have a number of resistors they can be connected in two different ways.

Connection in series

Fig. 4 shows a circuit diagram for three bulbs connected in **series**. The bulbs follow on one after another in a single chain. If one bulb fails all of the bulbs go out because the circuit is broken. Christmas tree lights are usually wired in series.

The same amount of current flows at any point in the circuit. As the electrons go through each bulb they lose some energy owing to the resistance in the fine wire filament in the bulb. Each bulb in the circuit is dimmer than the previous bulbs in the circuit.

The sum of the individual voltages lost across each bulb equals the total voltage across the bulbs.

If each bulb has a resistance of 2 ohms, the total resistance is 6 ohms (i.e. 2 + 2 + 2, the sum of the resistances).

Connection in parallel

Fig. 5 shows the same three bulbs connected in **parallel**. The current flowing through the circuit is divided so that some goes through each bulb. Because the three bulbs have the same resistance, equal currents flow through each bulb. This is not always the case.

The total resistance of three resistors (R) connected in parallel can be calculated using the equation:

$$\frac{1}{R} = \frac{1}{R_1} + \frac{1}{R_2} + \frac{1}{R_3}$$

where R_1, R_2, and R_3 are the resistances of the three resistors.

Example In Fig. 5:

$$\frac{1}{R} = \frac{3}{2}$$

$$R = \frac{2}{3} \text{ohms}$$

The advantage of a parallel circuit is that if one bulb fails, the others remain alight. However, it is more expensive to set up as it uses more wire and it is more complicated. It also uses more electricity.

Household wiring is usually connected in parallel. If it were in series, when you switched off one appliance everything in the house would go off!

In many cases a wiring system consists of parallel and series wiring.

Effects of electric current

There are three main effects of an electric current flowing. These are a magnetic effect, a heating effect and a chemical effect.

Magnetic effect

When an electric current passes through a wire it produces a magnetic field around the wire (p. 42).

Heating effect

When an electric current passes through a wire the wire heats up. In a circuit a **fuse** is often included as a safety device. The fuse contains a wire which melts and breaks the circuit if it overheats for any reason.

Chemical effect

Electricity can split up chemicals and cause chemical reactions to occur. This is called **electrolysis** (pp. 172-3). Chemicals react together in a cell, or battery, and produce electricity. Fig. 6 shows a simple cell with zinc and copper rods dipping into sulphuric acid. As the cell is used, the zinc rod is worn away.

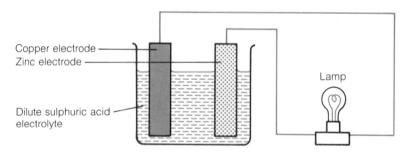

Copper electrode
Zinc electrode
Lamp
Dilute sulphuric acid electrolyte

Fig. 6 A simple cell

Direct current (dc) and alternating current (ac)

The electricity produced from the battery in Fig. 2 is called **direct current**. The positive and negative terminals are fixed throughout and the current flows in one direction all of the time.

Imagine that the connections on the battery were turned round over and over again. The direction of the current would constantly change. This is called **alternating current** (ac). Household electricity is ac and changes direction of flow 50 times each second. This is called the **frequency** of 50 hertz (Hz). This frequency is set in the power station.

A cathode ray oscilloscope (CRO) can be used to distinguish ac and dc currents. A CRO is a very fast acting voltmeter which works with ac or dc.

Fig. 7 shows the basic controls of a cathode ray oscilloscope. These are used to get a beam or **trace** which crosses the screen. Fig. 8 shows the traces which would be obtained with 4 V ac and 4 V dc electrical supplies.

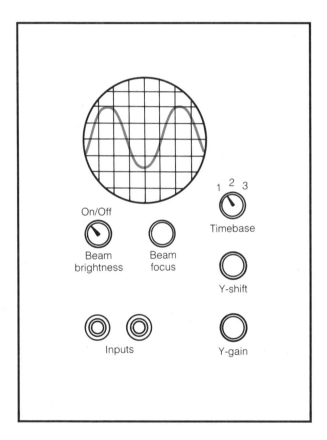

Fig. 7 Controls on a CRO

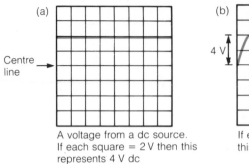

Centre line →

4 V

(a) A voltage from a dc source. If each square = 2 V then this represents 4 V dc

(b) If each square = 2 V, then this trace represents 4 V ac

Fig. 8 Traces on a CRO

Ohm's law

Ohm's law links together current (in A), potential difference (in V) and resistance (in ohms).
Ohm's law states that:

Potential difference = Current × Resistance.

Supply and distribution of electricity

Electricity produced in a power station is transmitted around the country by the National Grid system, by means of overhead or underground cables. The electricity is transmitted at voltages of up to 400 000 V. Using such a high voltage means lower currents have to be transmitted. The energy loss is less with lower currents.

There would be more heat loss if electricity were transmitted at lower voltages.

The voltage of the electricity is stepped down to a household voltage of 240 V using a **transformer** at a substation near to several houses. Transformers only operate with ac sources and this is the main reason for household supplies being ac.

Ring main circuits

The electricity entering the house is supplied to a main junction box. This permits a total current of about 60 A to flow. If the current exceeds this, the main fuse or trip will cut off all electricity.

The electricity is then distributed using **ring mains**. In a typical house there may be five ring mains:

● downstairs sockets
● downstairs lights
● upstairs sockets
● upstairs lights
● electric cooker.

Fig. 9 shows a simple ring main. Each ring main is protected by its own fuse or **circuit breaker**. If the current exceeds a certain value the fuse will blow or the circuit breaker will 'trip'. For lighting circuits a fuse of 5 A is suitable but for power circuits 30 A is more usual.

Three wires run around the house in a ring. The live wire (L) is brown in colour. It is most dangerous. Mains voltage can kill. The neutral wire (N) is blue in colour. It also carries a current but because it is earthed back at the power station, its voltage is not as high as the live wire. The earth wire (E) is green and yellow. This only carries a current if there is a fault in the circuit.

Separate fused three-pin plugs are plugged into the circuit for each appliance in use.

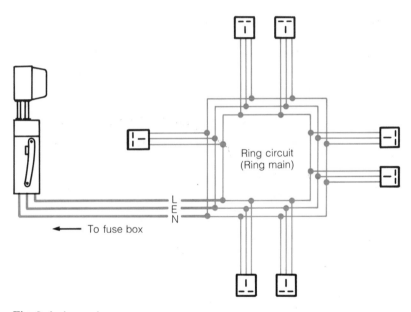

Fig. 9 A ring main

Wiring a three-pin plug

Fig. 10 shows a three-pin plug wired correctly. The brown wire on the appliance is connected to the live pin. The blue wire is connected to the neutral pin and the green and yellow wire is connected to the earth pin at the top of the plug.

The cord grip is intended to hold the cable in place and prevent the wires from pulling out of the terminal.

The earth connection is to ensure that in the event of a fault in the appliance, when a live wire touches a metal part of the casing, the electricity will flow safely away. Otherwise the user could get a fatal shock by touching the metal case. Not all appliances have earth wires. If earth wires are fitted they should be connected to the correct terminal in the battery.

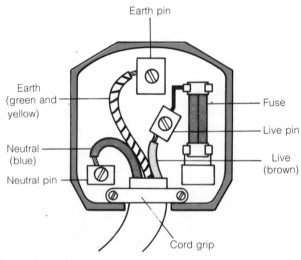

Fig. 10 Wiring a plug

It is important to use a fuse of the correct rating. Table 1 shows the fuse which should be fitted to different appliances.

For powers up to 750 W, 3 A fuse	For powers up to 3 KW, 13 A fuse
television	electric fire
record player	kettle
table lamp	toaster
food mixer	hair drier
drill	iron

Table 1

You can calculate the current flowing in an appliance by using the formula:

$$\text{Current} = \frac{\text{Power}}{\text{Voltage}}$$

Example Calculate the current used by a 60 W electric light bulb.

$$\text{Current} = \frac{60}{240} \text{ A}$$
$$= 0 \cdot 25 \text{ A}$$

Fuses commonly available are 1 A, 3 A, 5 A, 10 A and 13 A. Choose the fuse which is just above or closest above to the current used. In the example above, a 1 A fuse would be used. The fuse would blow if the current reached 1 A which it should never do if the bulb is operating properly.

The cost of electricity

We all have to pay for the electricity we use. The amount you have to pay depends upon:

(a) how many appliances are being used;
(b) how long they are used for;
(c) what the power rating of each appliance is;
(d) the cost of electricity.

The power rating of an appliance is calculated by multiplying current (in A) by voltage (in V). The units are watts (W) or kilowatts (kW).

Power (in W) = Current (in A) × Voltage (in V)

The basic unit used for calculating the cost of electricity is the kilowatt-hour (kWh). This is the electricity used if 1000 W (or 1 kW) of electricity is used for 1 hour. Sometimes this is called 1 **unit** of electricity.

The cost of electricity is about 6p per unit. On top of this you usually have to pay a standing charge to cover administrative charges etc. Usually a lower rate is available for electricity used during the night. This is called Economy 7 and is available because the demand for electricity is lower overnight and electricity boards are able to generate electricity cheaper.

Example What would be the cost of using a 3 kW electric fire for 10 hours? (Electricity costs 6p per unit.)

Quantity of electricity used = 3 × 10 kWh
$$= 30 \text{ units}$$
Cost = 30 × 6p = £1.80

Using electricity safely

1 Always switch off electricity at the mains before attempting any electrical repair.
2 If in any doubt leave repairs to an expert electrician.
3 Never allow electrics come in contact with water or wet hands. Do not use mains electrical equipment in a bathroom.
4 Never make temporary repairs using makeshift materials, or use broken sockets etc.
5 Never overload circuits by using adaptors.
6 Do not attempt to use appliances which use large amounts of electricity (e.g. a washing machine) on a lighting circuit.

Summary

An electric current is a flow of electrons around a circuit from the negative terminal of the electricity supply to the positive. The current is detected by a bulb or with an **ammeter** which measures the current in amps (A).

An energy supply pushes the electrons around the circuit. This comes from a battery, a transformer or mains supply. The driving force is called the **potential difference** (pd) and is measured on a **voltmeter** in volts (V).

Resistance opposes the flow of electricity in a circuit. The units of resistance are ohms (Ω). Resistors can be connected in **series** or in **parallel**. In series the bulbs follow on one after another in a single chain. If one bulb fails all of the bulbs go out. The same amount of current flows at any point and each built is dimmer than the previous bulbs. When the resistors are connected in parallel the current flowing through the circuit is divided so that some goes through each bulb. Household wiring is usually in parallel. The three main effects of a current are magnetic, heating and chemical.

Household electricity is 240 V, 50 Hz ac. It is transmitted at high voltage and stepped down with a **transformer**. The electricity is distributed around the house using **ring mains**. Separate fused three-pin plugs are plugged into the ring main circuit for each appliance in use. When wiring a three-pin plug it is important to connect the correct wires to the correct terminals: brown (live); blue (neutral); and green and yellow (earth).

The earth is a safety device to prevent electric shocks. The power rating of an appliance is calculated using the formula:

Power (in W) = Current (in A) × Voltage (in V)

The unit of electricity is the kilowatt-hour (kWh). This is the electricity used if 1000 W (or 1 kW) of electricity is used for 1 hour.

Revision questions

1 Why do you think there is a separate ring main circuit for the electric cooker?

2 Fig. 11 shows a circuit diagram for a model of a circuit which exists in most houses.

(a) What will happen if either of the switches is operated once?

(b) Where in a house would you find this kind of circuit and why is it useful?

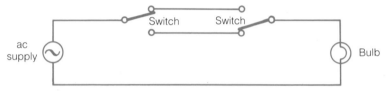

Fig. 11 A circuit diagram (question 2)

3 Fig. 12 shows a circuit diagram including five bulbs, A to E. Which bulbs would remain alight if:

(a) bulb A stopped working?

(b) bulb B stopped working?

(c) bulb C stopped working?

(d) bulb D stopped working?

(e) bulb E stopped working?

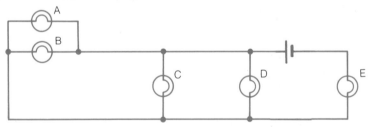

Fig. 12 A circuit diagram (question 3)

4 Complete Table 2. (1 unit of electricity costs 6p.)

Appliance	Power (in W)	pd (in V)	Current (in A)	Correct fuse (1 A, 3 A, 5 A, 10 A, 13 A)	Cost for 10 hours
Light bulb	100	240			
Television	200	240			
Fire		240	10		
Immersion	3000	240			

Table 2

5 A household uses 720 units of electricity. The cost per unit is 6p and the standing charge is £14. What is their bill?

6 Shanaz set up the circuit in Fig. 13 to measure the voltage across the resistor when different currents were passing through it. Her results are included in Table 3.

Voltage across R (in V)	Current through R (in A)
0.0	0.0
1.2	0.6
2.0	1.0
3.0	1.0
4.0	2.0
4.8	2.4

Table 3

(a) Name the pieces of apparatus labelled X and Y.
(b) Why was the variable resistor included in the circuit?
(c) Fig. 14 shows a graph of current against voltage. Four of the results are plotted on the graph. Plot the other two points and draw the best straight line through these points.
(d) Which result do you think is wrong? Explain the reason for your answer.
(e) What can you conclude about the relationship between current and voltage?
As voltage increases ....

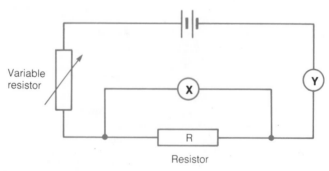

Fig. 13 Shanaz's circuit

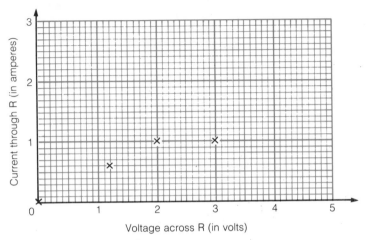

Fig. 14 Graph of current v voltage

3 Magnetism

Aims of the chapter

After reading this chapter you should:
1 Know that there are two magnetic poles and the test for magnetism is repulsion.
2 Be able to distinguish between magnetically hard and soft materials.
3 Know that like magnetic poles repel one another and unlike poles attract.
4 Know that the Earth behaves like a huge bar magnet.
5 Be able to describe an experiment to find the magnetic force pattern around a source of magnetism.
6 Be able to describe an experiment to show magnetic induction.
7 Be able to describe an experiment to show the magnetic effects of an electric current in a straight wire and a solenoid.
8 Know the right-hand-grab-rule and how it can be used to show the direction of a magnetic field.

9 Be able to describe the principles involved in the operation of a number of magnetic and electromagnetic devices, e.g. electric bell, electromagnetic relay, electric motor, generator and alternator, tape recorder, transformer.

Magnetism

K Magnetism is an effect of one thing on another. A magnet is a source of magnetism. The area around a magnet where the effects of the magnet can be noticed is called a **magnetic field**. The best magnets are made of steel, iron, cobalt or nickel. Steel holds its magnetism better than other materials and is called a **magnetically hard material**. Iron, on the other hand, loses its magnetism easily and is called a **magnetically soft material**.

Magnets do not attract metals such as aluminium, copper, tin and zinc. A magnet can be used to separate steel and aluminium cans during recycling.

The magnetic field around a bar magnet consists of a series of **lines of force**. The magnetic field can be found in two ways:

1 *Using a plotting compass (Fig. 1)*
A small plotting compass is moved around the magnet and the position of the compass needle is marked frequently. The direction of the compass needle always points along the lines of force in the magnetic field.

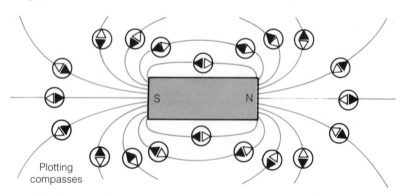

Plotting compasses

Fig. 1 Using a plotting compass

2 *Using iron filings (Fig. 2)*

A piece of paper is placed over the magnet. Iron filings (small grains of iron) are sprinkled onto the paper. The paper is tapped gently and the iron filings follow the lines of force. Fig. 2 shows the results which would be obtained with a bar magnet.

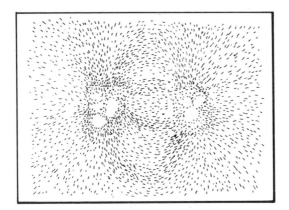

Fig. 2 Using iron filings

You will notice that the magnetic field is concentrated near the ends of the magnet. The lines of force in Fig. 1 appear to start from one end of the magnet. We call this the **north-seeking pole** or **north pole**. The lines of force go to the **south-seeking pole** or **south pole** at the other end of the magnet.

If two magnets are brought close together so that the north pole of one approaches the south pole of the other, there is a force of **attraction** between them. Fig. 3 shows the magnetic field around the two magnets. The two magnetic fields join together.

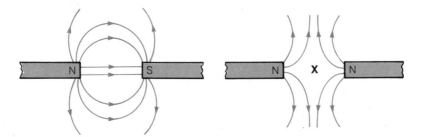

Fig. 3 Magnetic attraction   **Fig. 4** Magnetic repulsion

However, if two north poles are brought close together there is a force of **repulsion**. The magnetic fields cancel each other out (Fig. 4) and between the magnets is a neutral point (marked X) where there is no magnetic force. Similar results would be obtained if two south poles were brought close together.

The Earth's magnetic field

If a magnet is suspended freely so that it can rotate, the magnet lines up with its north pole pointing north and its south pole pointing south. This could be explained if there were a huge magnet in the Earth. A magnet suspended and free to rotate is the principle of the compass. However, a free magnet does not point exactly north-south. The magnet points to the **magnetic north** rather than the **geographic north**. The difference in Britain is an angle of about 7° (Fig. 5).

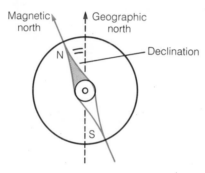

Fig. 5 Magnetic and geographic north

Magnetic induction

If a magnet is dipped into a pile of nails, a number of nails will cling onto it (Fig. 6). The first nail on the magnet receives some of the magnetism and passes some on to other nails. The idea of magnetism being passed on from one subject to another is called **magnetic induction**. Magnetic induction will only occur if the materials (magnet and nails in this case) are touching.

   The only true test of magnetism is **repulsion**. Attraction between a piece of metal and a magnet may be due to magnetic induction rather than the piece of metal being a magnet.

Electromagnetism

When an electric current is passing through a wire it produces an **electromagnetic field** around the wire. This was first discovered in 1819 by Hans Christian Oersted.

   If dc is used the electromagnetic field will be in one direction only. The magnetic field is shown in Fig. 7.

The direction of the magnetic field can be found using the **right-hand-grab-rule**. When the wire is gripped with the right hand, with the thumb pointing in the direction of the current, the fingers show the direction of the magnetic field (Fig. 8).

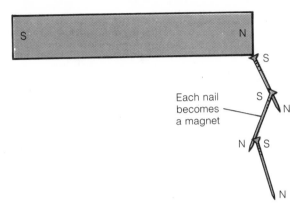

Fig. 6 Magnetic induction

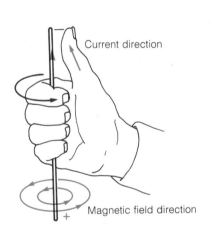

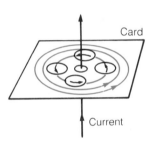

Fig. 7 Magnetic field around a wire

Fig. 8 The right-hand-grab-rule

The magnetic field produced by a wire is relatively weak. A stronger field can be produced by winding the wire into a coil and producing a **solenoid**. The magnetic field can be made stronger by putting a bar of soft iron in the middle of the coil, increasing the number of turns of wire or increasing the current. The resulting magnet, which has magnetic properties *only* when the current is flowing, is called an **electromagnet**. The coil of wire behaves like a bar magnet. If you grip the solenoid with your right hand, your thumb points to the north pole (Fig. 9).

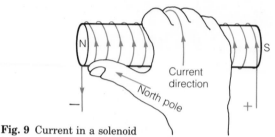

Fig. 9 Current in a solenoid

If ac is used, the magnetic field will alternate at the same rate.

A number of everyday objects rely upon electromagnetic effects:

The electric bell

Fig. 10 shows an electric bell. When the bell-push is pressed the circuit is completed. The electric current makes the coil into a magnet. This attracts the iron clanger towards it. The clanger strikes the bell and makes a sound. However, this separates the contact points and cuts off the current. The clanger returns to its original position and the procedure is repeated.

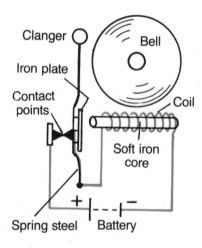

Fig. 10 The electric bell

Electromagnetic relays

An electromagnetic relay (Fig. 11) is a simple switch, operated by an electromagnet, which switches on and off a large current.

The input current magnetizes the electromagnet. The electromagnet attracts the soft iron **armature** (see p. 40). The armature moves and closes the contacts on the main circuit. When the input current is switched off, the armature returns to its original position and the current in the main circuit is cut off.

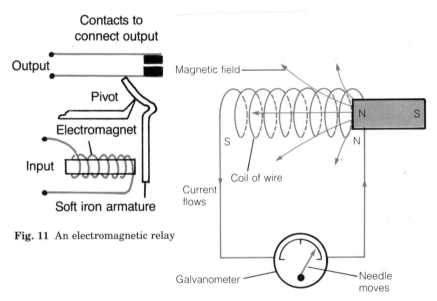

Fig. 11 An electromagnetic relay

Fig. 12 Detecting small currents

Tape recorders

The recording head of a tape recorder is an electromagnet. The sound is converted by the microphone into an electrical signal. The signal switches the recording head on and off. The electromagnetism created by the electromagnet in the head is recorded on the tape. The tape is coated with a magnetic material.

Making electricity with a magnet

When a magnet is moved in and out of a coil of wire an electric current is made (Fig. 12). The current is small and can be detected with a sensitive meter called a **galvanometer**. When the meter is pushed into the coil the needle on the galvanometer moves one way. When the magnet is removed, the needle moves the other way.

When a magnet is moved near a suitable conductor, an electric current is produced. This is called **electromagnetic induction**.

Generators

A generator converts kinetic energy into electrical energy. There are
two types of generator.
(a) A **dc generator** produces dc electricity, e.g. a bicycle **dynamo**.
(b) An **ac generator** or alternator produces ac electricity in a power
station or a car.

In a bicycle dynamo, a magnet rotates near a coil of wire which is
wound on a soft iron core. A current is set up in the circuit which
includes the coil of wire (Fig. 13). It is easier to rotate the magnet, as
rotating the coil would need some system for preventing the twisting
of the wires. The faster the magnet rotates the greater will be the
current produced.

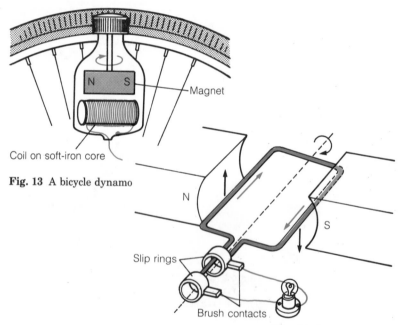

Magnet

Coil on soft-iron core

Fig. 13 A bicycle dynamo

N

S

Slip rings

Brush contacts

Fig. 14 An ac generator

A simple ac generator or alternator is shown in Fig. 14. It has a
rotating coil and a fixed magnet. As the coil rotates, a current is
induced. The brush contacts enable the coil to rotate whilst
maintaining contact with the rest of the electrical circuit. Three ways
of increasing the current are:
(a) spinning the coil faster;
(b) using a stronger magnet;
(c) using more turns of wire on the coil.

Electric motor

When a wire carrying an electric current passes through a magnetic field, a force acts on the wire and it moves. The direction of movement can be predicted using **Fleming's left-hand rule** (Fig. 15). This is the principle on which the simple dc electric motor is based (Fig. 16). A motor turns electrical energy into kinetic energy.

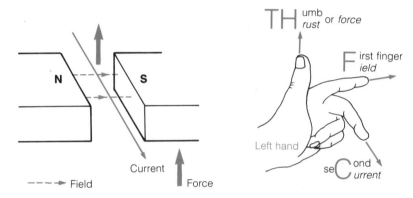

Fig. 15 Fleming's left-hand rule

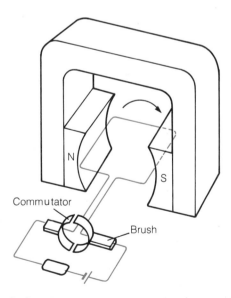

Fig. 16 A simple dc motor

When the electric current passes through the coil it produces a magnetic field. The interaction of this magnetic field and the field of the permanent magnet makes the coil move. The only possible movement is rotation and so the coil rotates. The motion is continuous and in one direction. The direction can be predicted by Fleming's left-hand rule. If the direction of the current is reversed, the coil rotates in the opposite direction. The coil can be made to rotate faster by:
(a) increasing the current;
(b) using a stronger magnet;
(c) using more turns of wire on the coil.
The brushes are used to maintain electrical contact with the spinning coil. The commutator rotates and makes sure that whichever wire is nearer the north pole of the magnet, it always has the current moving in the same direction, so ensuring the coil rotates in the same direction.

Electric motors used in everyday appliances such as electric drills, washing machines and food mixers usually have several coils wound onto one core. This is called an **armature**. Each of the coils has its own commutator. The additional coils make a stronger magnetic field and the resulting motor runs smoothly and with a more powerful turning effect.

Transformers

A transformer changes the voltage of an alternating current. It can either increase the voltage (a 'step-up' transformer) or decrease the voltage (a 'step-down' transformer).

A transformer consists of a metal core with two coils of wire wrapped around it. The coils will usually have different numbers of turns. One coil is connected to the ac supply. This creates a magnetic field inside the coil. The second coil is affected by this changing magnetic field. In this coil the reverse happens. Fig. 17 shows a step-up transformer. The voltage induced in the secondary coil can be calculated using the formula:

$$\frac{\text{Voltage across secondary coil}}{\text{Voltage across primary coil}} = \frac{\text{No. of turns on secondary coil}}{\text{No. of turns on primary coil}}$$

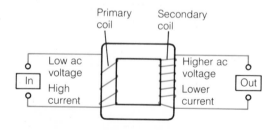

Fig. 17 A step-up transformer

Summary

Magnets can attract or repel other substances in their **magnetic fields**. Magnets do not attract metals such as aluminium, copper, tin or zinc. The magnetic field around a bar magnet consists of a series of **lines of force**. A bar magnet has a north-seeking pole at one end and a south- seeking pole at the other. Two similar poles brought close together repel one another but two different poles attract. The Earth acts like a big bar magnet. Magnets can pass on some of their magnetism to iron or steel objects in contact and make them magnetic. This is called **magnetic induction**.

When an electric current is passing through a wire it produces an **electromagnetic field** and produces an electromagnet, which has similar effects to an ordinary magnet, when an electric current is passing. The magnetic field produced by a wire is relatively weak but a stronger field can be produced by winding the wire into a coil and producing a **solenoid**. A bar of soft iron in the middle of the coil strengthens the field. When a magnet is moved in a coil of wire an electric current is made. This is called **electromagnetic induction**.

A **generator** converts kinetic energy into electrical energy. When a wire carrying an electric current passes through a magnetic field, a force acts on the wire and it moves. A dc electric motor turns electrical energy into kinetic energy.

Revision questions

1 Fig. 18 shows an alarm system. When the window is forced, it opens the switch labelled S. Describe what happens when this switch is opened.

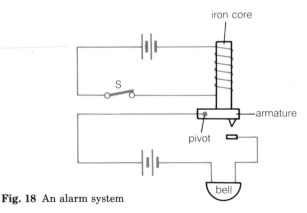

Fig. 18 An alarm system

2 Fig. 19 shows the outline of the workings of a meter used to measure electric current in a circuit. Inside the coil are two iron bars. One is fixed and the other is on the end of a pivoted pointer.
(a) Apart from heat, what is produced inside the coil when electricity is passing?
(b) Explain what happens to the two iron bars.
(c) What is the purpose of the hairspring?

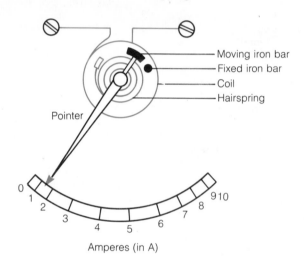

Fig. 19 The workings of a meter

3 A transformer has 300 turns on the primary coil and an input voltage of 240 V. The secondary coil has 50 turns on it.
(a) Is the transformer a 'step-down' or 'step-up'? Explain your answer.
(b) Calculate the output voltage.
(c) Name one household appliance which might have this kind of transformer.

4 Waves

Aims of the chapter

After reading this chapter you should:
1 Know that a wave is one way of carrying energy from one place to another.
2 Be able to distinguish between transverse and longitudinal waves.
3 Know the meaning of the terms *frequency, wavelength, amplitude* and *velocity*.
4 Know that sound waves are longitudinal waves.
5 Know some of the properties and uses of sound waves.
6 Be able to describe different types of electromagnetic waves.
7 Be able to distinguish reflection and refraction.
8 Be able to distinguish real and virtual images.
9 Know that white light can be split up or dispersed by a prism.
10 Be able to explain the working of the eye and the ear.

Waves

A wave is a way of transferring energy from one place to another without transferring matter. Sound waves, water waves and seismic waves (during earthquakes) are examples of wave motion. Other forms of wave energy – including X-rays, ultraviolet rays, light, microwaves and radiowaves – are grouped together under a heading of **electromagnetic waves**.

There are two kinds of waves, **transverse** and **longitudinal**, which depend upon the vibrations that cause the waves. It is important to be clear about the differences between the two.

Transverse and longitudinal waves

The word **transverse** means across and a transverse wave moves across the direction of the wave. Ripples on a pond, waves on the sea and waves passing along a rope are transverse waves (Fig. 1).

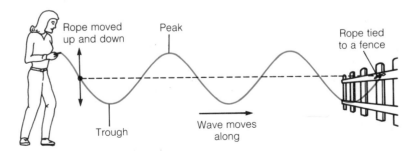

Rope moved up and down

Peak

Rope tied to a fence

Trough

Wave moves along

Fig. 1 Transverse waves

In the case of the rope, the rope itself is moving up and down but the energy is being transferred *along* the rope. Similarly, a cork bobs up and down in the sea as the waves move past it.
All electromagnetic waves are also transverse waves.

Energy transfer ——▶

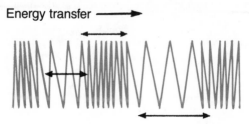

Fig. 2 Longitudinal waves

Sound waves are the only example of **longitudinal waves**. Fig. 2 shows a longitudinal wave. The energy is passed along the wave but the particles are moving from left to right and from right to left. Longitudinal waves need a substance or **medium** to pass through. They move much more slowly than transverse waves. Transverse waves do not need a medium to travel through and can travel through a vacuum. They can move very fast.

Amplitude and wavelength

If one end of a rope is tied to a fence and the other end is moved up and down, a transverse wave is set up. Fig. 3 shows a graph of the distance of particles from the centre (called the **displacement**) at various places along the wave. The wave consists of a series or **peaks** and **troughs**. The height of the wave is called its **amplitude**.

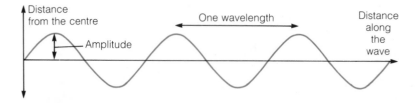

Fig. 3 Graph of displacement of particles

The **wavelength** (Greek letter lambda λ) is the distance between two adjacent peaks. It is measured in metres (m).

The **frequency** of a wave is the number of complete waves made in one second. The symbol for frequency is *f* and the units are **hertz** (Hz). The higher the frequency of a wave the shorter its wavelength becomes.

The **speed** of a wave can be worked out from the wavelength and frequency.

Wave speed (in m/s) = Frequency (in Hz) × Wavelength (in m)

Example Find the wave speed of a wave with frequency 100 Hz and wavelength 2m.
f = 100 Hz, λ = 2 m
Wave speed = $f\lambda$
$\qquad$ = 100 × 2 = 200 m/s

Sound waves

Sound waves need a medium to pass through. Sound travels in air by compressing the air at some points of the wave and stretching it at other points (Fig. 4).

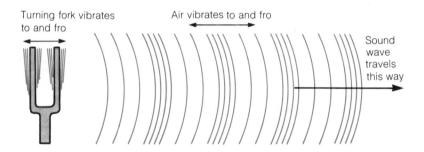

Turning fork vibrates to and fro

Air vibrates to and fro

Sound wave travels this way

Fig. 4 Sound waves

Sound waves travel faster through some materials than others. Through air sound travels at about 330 m/s but through water sound travels about five times faster.

Sound waves travel more slowly than light waves. During a thunderstorm you *see* the lightning before you *hear* the thunder.

When sound waves meet a solid surface they are **reflected**. The reflected sound waves are called **echoes**. Echoes can be used to find the depth of the sea bed by beaming sound waves to the sea bed and timing how long it takes for the echo to return to the ship on the surface (Fig. 5). Similar principles are used by geologists searching for underground deposits of petroleum and by bats judging distances when flying.

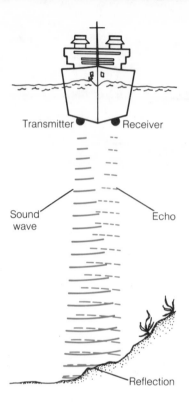

Fig. 5 Echoes

The electromagnetic spectrum

Fig. 6 shows the different types of electromagnetic radiation and their uses. The forms of radiation with high frequency transfer larger amounts of energy.

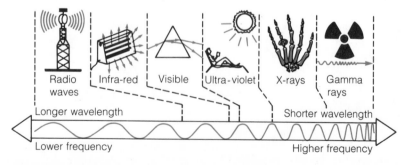

Fig. 6 Types of electromagnetic radiation

Reflection

When a wave hits a barrier it is reflected. This reflection is clearly shown using light waves. Fig. 7 shows what happens when a light ray strikes a flat mirror (called a *plane* mirror). The **angle of incidence** (shown as i in the diagram) and the **angle of reflection** (r) are always equal. The line at right angles to the mirror is called the **normal** line.

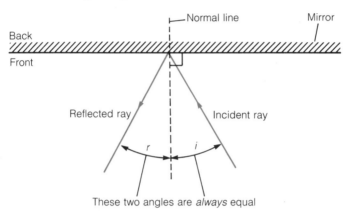

Fig. 7 Reflection at a plane mirror

The image appears as far behind the mirror as the object is in front of it. The image is reversed or back-to-front. Fig. 8 shows how the image is formed. The image is **virtual**. This means it can be seen but it cannot be focused on a screen.

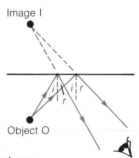

Fig. 8 Formation of an image

Refraction

Waves pass at different speeds through different media. When a wave passes from one medium to another, bending occurs. This is called **refraction**.

Again, refraction can be clearly shown with light rays (Fig. 9). Light rays bend when they enter a glass block and bend again when they leave the glass block. Light refracts *towards* the normal as it enters the glass: as light travels faster through air than through glass. On leaving the glass it bends *away* from the normal. If the light strikes the glass block at right angles, the ray passes through the block unchanged.

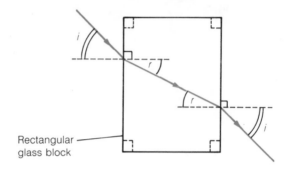

Rectangular glass block

Fig. 9 Light refracted through a glass block

The spectrum

White light is made up from seven different colours, each of which has a different wavelength. When a ray of light enters a prism, the light is split up or **dispersed** because the different colours bend by different amounts (Fig. 10). The resulting array of separate colours is called a **spectrum** and can be seen in rainbows. If the separate colours are mixed, white light is produced.

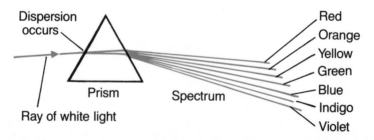

Fig. 10 Dispersion

The eye

An eye (Fig. 11) contains a piece of shaped transparent material called a **convex lens**. The lens focuses the light rays on the **retina**. The retina cells are stimulated by light and messages are sent to the brain via the **optic nerve**. The **ciliary muscles** of the eye can alter the shape of the lens. This enables the eye to focus clearly on objects at different distances. This is called **accommodation**.

If the eye becomes unable to focus the light rays onto the retina, spectacles may be needed.

The image produced on the retina is upside-down and is called a **real** image.

The **iris** controls the amount of light which enters the eye by making the **pupil** – the hole in the centre – larger or smaller. When it is large more light enters, when it is small, less light enters.

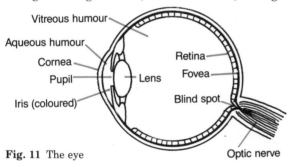

Fig. 11 The eye

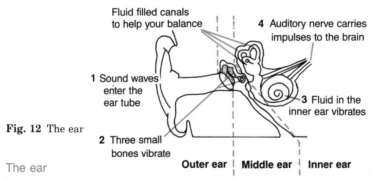

Fig. 12 The ear

The ear

Fig. 12 shows how the ear works. The eardrum is able to detect the compressions and stretchings of the air caused by sound waves. The vibrations of the eardrum are passed through the three small bones called **ossicles** in the middle ear and magnified. The fluid in the inner ear then vibrates and messages are passed on via the auditory nerve to the brain.

Summary

A wave transfers energy without transferring matter. Waves can be **transverse** or **longitudinal**, depending upon the vibrations that cause them. A transverse wave transfers energy along the wave as the particles move up and down. Ripples on a pond are transverse waves. Sound waves are the only example of longitudinal waves, where the energy is passed along the wave but the particles are moving left to right and right to left. Longitudinal waves need a **medium** to pass through. Sound passes through the air by compressing the air at some parts of the wave and stretching at other parts. Transverse waves do not need a medium to travel through and can travel through a vacuum. They can move very fast.

The wave consists of a series of **peaks** and **troughs**. The height of the wave is called its **amplitude** and the distance between two adjacent peaks is the **wavelength** (λ). The **frequency** of a wave (f) is the number of wavelengths that pass a fixed point in 1 second.

The most important transverse waves are electromagnetic waves. These include radio waves, microwaves, infra-red rays, light, ultra-violet, X-rays and γ rays.

When a light ray strikes a flat mirror, **reflection** takes place. The **angle of incidence** is always equal to the **angle of reflection**. The bending of light rays is called **refraction**. When a ray of light enters a prism, the light is **dispersed**. Lights of different colours are seen.

The eye is a means of the body detecting light waves and the ear is a means of detecting sound waves.

Revision questions

1 A colour television is based on three different primary colours – red, blue and green. Fig. 13 shows how different primary colours can be mixed together to make other colours.
Which colours mix together to produce:
(a) yellow light?
(b) magenta light?
(c) cyan blue light?
(d) white light?

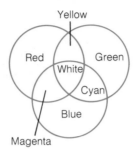

Fig. 13 Mixing colours

2 Explain why during the timing of an athletics race the timekeeper ·
is told to watch for the puff of smoke from the gun rather than listen
for the sound.

5 Force and motion

Aims of the chapter

After reading this chapter you should:
1 Know that forces are measured in newtons and act in pairs.
2 Know weight is a force caused by gravitational field.
3 Be able to distinguish between mass, force and pressure.
4 Know that pressure is measured in pascals (N/m^2).
5 Know that the atmosphere has weight and exerts a pressure.
6 Be able to distinguish between speed and velocity.
7 Be able to distinguish between constant speed, acceleration and
deceleration so that graphs can be interpreted.
8 Be able to demonstrate a practical knowledge of the effects of forces
in everyday life.

Forces

We shall see later that forces are at work everywhere. Forces are
responsible for either starting things or stopping things. For example,
a force is needed to push a car which has broken down and a force is
needed to stop a car which has started to roll down a hill. Pushing and
pulling are types of force. Forces are measured in newtons (N) using a
newtonmeter.

A newtonmeter (Fig. 1) is a spring which extends when a force is
applied. The bigger the force the more the spring extends.

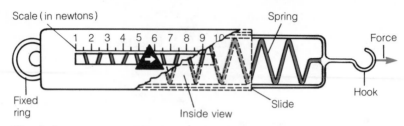

Fig. 1 A newtonmeter

Force is a **vector** quantity because a force always acts in a definite direction. Forces act in pairs: for example, if you are standing on the floor you exert a force on the floor but the floor exerts an equal force upwards which stops you sinking into the ground!

Weight is a common force. A bag of granulated sugar has **mass** of 1 kg. If we hang it on a newtonmeter we find the **force** exerted is about 10 N. The force pulling down on the bag of sugar is caused by the gravitational field of the Earth. If the bag of sugar is taken to the Moon, the mass is still 1 kg but its weight is less than 2 N because the gravitational field on the Moon is about one sixth of that of the Earth. In space where there is no gravity, the bag of sugar (still mass 1 kg) has no weight at all: i.e. it is weightless.

Weight can be calculated using the equation:

Weight (in N) = Mass (in kg) × Acceleration due to gravity (in m/s^2)

$$W = mg$$

For the earth, g is about 10 m/s^2.

A mass of 5 kg, therefore, exerts a force pushing down of 50 N. If the mass rests on a table, there must be a force of 50 N pushing upwards.

Satellites orbiting the Earth follow circular paths. The gravitational force of the Earth keeps the satellite in orbit.

Pressure

Pressure is the spreading out of a force on a surface. In Fig. 2 a block of metal of mass 1 kg is standing on a surface in two different ways. The block has dimensions 10 cm × 10 cm × 2 cm. The block exerts a force of 10 N downwards due to gravity. However, in (a) the force is exerted on an area of 100 cm^2 (10 cm × 10 cm) but in (b) on an area of 20 cm^2 (2 cm × 10 cm).

Pressure is the force which acts on a single unit of area. In (a) the pressure is 10 ÷ 100 = 0.1 N/cm^2 and in (b) the pressure is 10 ÷ 20 = 0.5 N/cm^2.

A force concentrated on a small area will exert a much larger pressure than the same force acting on a large area.

Units of pressure are N/cm^2 or N/m^2:

1 N/m^2 = 1 pascal (Pa)

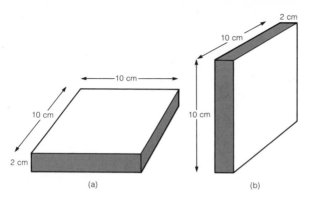

Fig. 2 Different forces exerted by the same block

(a)   (b)

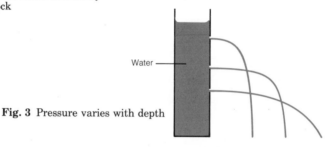

Fig. 3 Pressure varies with depth

Water

The pascal is the common unit of pressure.

In solids, pressure acts only in the direction of the force. Stiletto heels damage floors more than ordinary heels because, although the force is the same, the area in contact with the floor is much smaller. The pressure is therefore much greater. In liquids and gases the pressure acts in all directions.

If a force is applied to a fluid (liquid or a gas) it is transmitted through the fluid to the walls of the container. In a liquid the pressure increases as the depth of the liquid increases. This can be shown using a tin can as in Fig. 3.

The same is true for gases. The pressure of the Earth's atmosphere decreases as height above the Earth's surface increases. We can think of the atmosphere as a column of air 10 km high. This column has weight and provides a downward force.

Fig. 4(a) shows a **barometer** which can be used to measure the pressure of air. The pressure of air is balanced by the pressure of a column of mercury about 76 cm high. As air pressure changes so the height of the mercury column will change slightly. Fig. 4(b) shows a **manometer** used to measure gas pressure. The gas pressure forces some of the liquid from the left-hand side of the manometer to the right. The difference in levels is a measure of the pressure of the gas.

In a car braking system, the pressure applied to the brake in the car is transmitted to the brakes on the wheels by liquid.

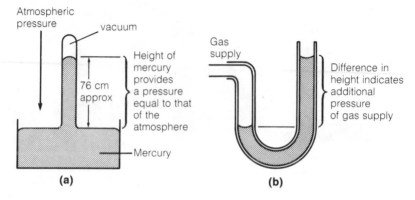

Fig. 4 Measuring pressure

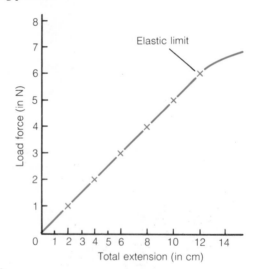

Fig. 5 Hooke's law

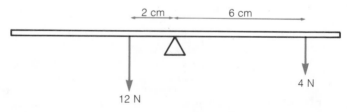

Fig. 6 A simple lever

Effects of forces

Forces can change the:
(a) shape or size of an object;
(b) direction of movement of an object;
(c) speed of an object.

A force can change the shape or size of an object. The changing of the shape of an object is called **deformation**. The force may change the shape of an object either temporarily or permanently. If the change is temporary it is sometimes called **elastic deformation**. A spring, for example, is extended when a force is applied. When the force is removed the spring returns to its original shape. However, if the spring is extended too far, beyond its **elastic limit**, it will not return to its original shape and will be spoiled for ever. Fig. 5 shows a graph obtained when different forces are applied to a spring and the extension is measured. From these results we can conclude that the extension of the spring is **directly proportional** to the force applied, provided the elastic limit has not been exceeded. Directly proportional means that the extension goes up as the force goes up. This statement is called **Hooke's law**.

Forces can also squeeze or compress an object.

Forces can change the movement of an object. For example, a force applied to the end of a spanner can turn a tight nut. The turning effect depends upon both the size of the force and the length of the spanner. The turning effect of a force is called its **moment** or **torque**. The moment of a force is calculated using the formula:

Moment = Force × Perpendicular distance from force to turning point
(in Nm)   (in N)   (in m)

The turning point is called the **pivot** or **fulcrum**.

On a see-saw when it is balanced, the clockwise and anticlockwise moments are equal. In Fig. 6 the clockwise moment (i.e. the right-hand side) is $6 \times 4 = 24$ Nm and the anticlockwise moment (i.e. the left-hand side) is $2 \times 12 = 24$ Nm. The see-saw is balanced. If the 4 N force is moved 7 metres from the fulcrum on the right-hand side, the clockwise moment becomes $4 \times 7 = 28$ Nm and the right-hand side will go down.

Many household items rely on turning moments, e.g. crowbars, wheelbarrows, nutcrackers, scissors etc.

Speed is the rate a body moves from place to place. It is a distance measured in an amount of time. It may be measured in a variety of units (e.g. miles per hour (mph), km per second (km/s), metres per second (m/s) etc).

$$\text{Speed} = \frac{\text{Distance}}{\text{Time}}$$

The terms **speed** and **velocity** are often confused. Velocity is a vector quantity and is speed in a *certain direction*. Speed is not a vector quantity and no direction is specified.

Fig. 7(a) shows a graph of distance (on the y-axis) against time for a car moving at a constant velocity of 30 m/s. (This is labelled A.) You will notice that the distance travelled each second is the same (30 m). In Fig. 7(b) the same car is shown in the graph, labelled A. This is a graph of velocity against time. The graph is horizontal (i.e. parallel to the x-axis) as the speed is not changing.

Another car B is shown in the two graphs. You will notice that this car is *not* moving with constant velocity throughout. After 10 seconds the car speeds up or **accelerates**, i.e. every second it is travelling faster. Acceleration is measured in units of m/s^2. Acceleration can be calculated using the equation:

$$\text{Acceleration (in m/s}^2) = \frac{\text{Increase in velocity (in m/s)}}{\text{Time for the increase in velocity (in s)}}$$

Slowing down is called **deceleration**. It has the same units as acceleration but whereas acceleration is always positive, deceleration is always negative.

An object stays at rest (i.e. not moving) or moves at a constant speed in a straight line unless a force acts upon it. Forces can make stationary objects start to move or alter the speed and/or direction of a moving object.

Force (in N) = Mass (in kg) × Acceleration (in m/s^2)

Acceleration therefore depends upon the force applied (in N) and the mass of the object (in kg).

When an object is rolling at a steady speed along a level surface it will come to rest. This is because of a force of **friction** which resists motion. When a car is rolling there is friction between the tyres and the road. Friction is necessary to keep the car safely on the road.

Summary

Pushing and pulling are types of **force**. Forces are measured in newtons (N) using a newtonmeter. Forces act in pairs. Weight is a common force which can be calculated by:

Weight = Mass × Acceleration due to gravity
W = mg

For the earth $g = 10$ m/s^2

Pressure is the force which acts on a single unit of area. A force concentrated on a small area will exert a much larger pressure than the same force acting on a large area. Units of pressure are N/cm^2 or N/m^2. 1 N/m^2 = 1 pascal (Pa). The pascal is the common unit of pressure.

In solids, pressure acts only in the direction of the force. In liquids

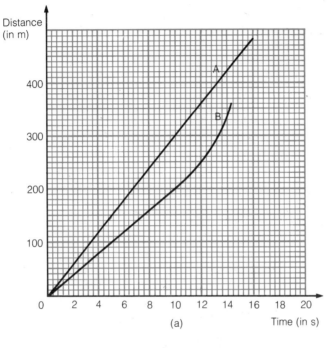

(a)

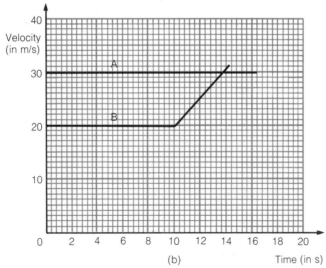

(b)

Fig. 7 Graphs

and gases, the pressure acts in all directions. In a liquid, the pressure increases as the depth of the liquid increases. The pressure of the Earth's atmosphere decreases as the height above the Earth's surface increases. A **barometer** can be used to measure the pressure of air. A **manometer** is used to measure gas pressure.

Forces can change the:

(a) shape or size of an object;
(b) direction of movement of an object;
(c) speed of an object.

Speed is a distance measured in an amount of time.

$$\text{Speed} = \frac{\text{Distance}}{\text{Time}}$$

Velocity is a vector quantity and is speed in a certain direction.

$$\textbf{Acceleration (in m/s}^2) = \frac{\text{Increase in velocity (in m/s)}}{\text{Time for the increase in velocity (in s)}}$$

Slowing down is called **deceleration** is always considered as negative acceleration. Acceleration depends upon the force applied (in N) and the mass of the object (in kg).

Revision questions

1 Calculate the acceleration of a 100 kg mass caused by a force of 300 N.

2 What is the average speed of a car which travels 160 miles from Stoke on Trent to London in 4 hours?

3 A car is travelling at 30 m/s. The driver then accelerates to 72 m/s in 7 seconds.

(a) What is the acceleration?
(b) The driver then has to brake suddenly and come to rest in 3 seconds. Calculate the deceleration.
(c) Explain why, without a seat belt, a driver might strike the windscreen during a rapid deceleration.

4 The Moon's gravitational field strength is about one sixth of that of the Earth. An object of mass 120 kg is weighed on the Earth and on the Moon.

(a) What is the weight of the object (in N) on the Earth?
(b) What is the mass of the object on the Moon?
(c) What is the weight of the object (in N) on the Moon?

5 Table 1 is similar to one in the Highway Code and shows the overall stopping distances at different car speeds.

Speed of car	10 m/s	15 m/s	20 m/s	25 m/s	30 m/s
Thinking distance	6 m	9 m		15 m	18 m
Braking distance	8 m	18 m		50 m	72 m
Overall stopping distance	14 m	27 m		65 m	90 m

Table 1

The stopping distance is the sum of the thinking distance and the braking distance.

(a) What do you think is meant by the term *thinking distance*?

(b) How does the thinking distance depend upon the speed of the car?

(c) What thinking distance corresponds to a speed of 20 m/s?

(d) Suggest, with reasons, the safe minimum distance that one car should stay behind another if both are travelling at 15 m/s.

(e) Fig. 8 shows a graph of braking distance against (speed of car)^2. From the graph find the braking distance for a car travelling at 20 m/s.

(f) Why is the graph in Fig. 8 a straight line?

(g) Why is the braking distance greater on wet roads?

(h) A car could be stopped by running it up a slope. If the car was travelling at 20 m/s, to what maximum vertical height, h, could it go before coming to rest? Assume that friction can be ignored.

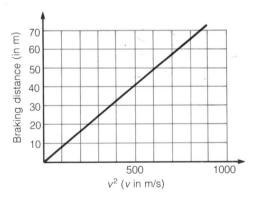

Fig. 8 Braking distance v speed

Aims of the chapter

After reading this chapter you should:
1 Understand the importance of controlling biological and physical systems.
2 Know that a control system involves a sensor, control mechanism and effector.
3 Be able to identify the sensor, control mechanism and effector in particular systems.
4 Be able to explain the regulation of temperature and water balance in a human being.
5 Be able to explain simple reflex actions.
6 Be able to explain how a thermostat with a bimetallic strip operates.
7 Know common components in electronic systems.
8 Be able to explain simple electronic circuits and devise simple examples.

Introduction

Throughout Science there are examples where systems have to be stable and controlled. We call this **homeostasis**, which means 'keeping constant conditions'. In biological systems failure to control conditions can cause illness or even death. In electrical, mechanical and chemical systems, breakdown may occur, often with dramatic results.

A machine which rolls metal to a constant thickness, for example, illustrates the three things necessary in any control system.

1 A **sensor** or **receptor** which detects any change from the set conditions. In the case considered, this would trigger if the metal were being rolled too thickly or too thinly.

2 A **control mechanism** which initiatives the necessary corrective measures.

3 An **effector** which brings about the necessary changes. In our example this would be a device which increases or decreases the pressure exerted by the rollers.

We shall see the same three things controlling other systems.

The sensor, control mechanism and effector communicate with one another and this is called **feedback**. This can be positive or negative. In our example, positive feedback from the sensors would result in a change in pressure on the rollers, i.e. a change is necessary. Negative feedback would mean that metal of the correct thickness is being rolled and no change is needed. Both sorts of message are important.

Control of body temperature

The **hypothalmus** in the brain controls temperature inside the human body. It monitors the temperature of the blood flowing through it. The brain then sets about starting procedures to either cool or warm the body. Fig. 1 shows a section of human skin. If the body is too hot, the blood capillaries widen to bring more blood to the skin where heat is radiated. More sweat is produced and when this evaporates, cooling occurs. (Remember evaporation requires energy, p. 115-17) Also, erector muscles relax and the hairs on the skin lie flat. There is moving air near the body so evaporation occurs quickly.

The reverse procedure occurs if the blood is too cold. The contraction of the erector muscles causes the hairs to stand up and 'goose pimples' are seen. Shivering also raises the temperature by producing heat in the muscles.

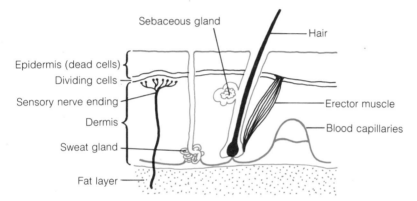

Fig. 1 Section of human skin

Osmoregulation

This is the control of the water content in our bodies. Water makes up about 60 to 70 per cent of our bodies and it is important that we maintain this. Loss of water can cause **dehydration**. We lose water from our bodies by three means.

1 Through our lungs when we breathe out water vapour.
2 Through our skin through sweating.
3 Through our kidneys in the urine which is produced.

We take in water in drinks and food. Water is produced in some processes in the body.

The organ which controls the amount of water leaving the body is the **kidney**. This can correct the amount of water in the body by adjusting the amount of urine. The kidney works in conjunction with the hypothalmus and the anti-diuretic hormone (ADH) to keep the balance of water in the body.

On a hot day, when more water vapour is lost from the lungs and more sweating occurs, the amount of urine is reduced. Increased ADH makes us feel thirsty and then we drink more water. On a cold day, however, more urine will be produced.

Reflexes

Reflex actions occur automatically and without thought. They enable us to respond quickly to danger. A **reflex arc** is a pathway along which the nervous impulses pass which are involved in the reflex action.

Suppose your finger touches a hot tripod. The automatic reflex removes your finger from the heat. Fig. 2 shows the situation.

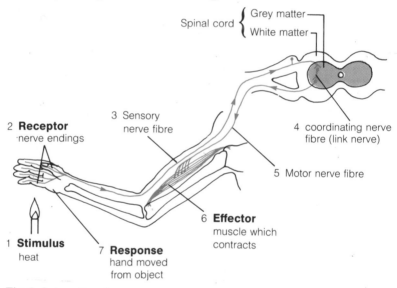

Spinal cord { Grey matter —
            { White matter ⌐

3 Sensory nerve fibre

2 **Receptor** ·nerve endings

4 coordinating nerve fibre (link nerve)

5 Motor nerve fibre

6 **Effector** muscle which contracts

1 **Stimulus** heat

7 **Response** hand moved from object

Fig. 2 Automatic reflex

Nerve endings in the skin of the fingers act as the receptors and note the danger. Nervous impulses are set up in the nerve fibre. Grey matter in the spinal cord acts as the control mechanism. The nerve fibres then carry a message to the muscle which acts as the effector and contracts the muscle. The finger is removed from the heat.

Thermostats

Many household appliances contain thermostats. The word 'thermostat' means still temperature. A thermostat maintains a steady temperature and, because it switches off the appliance when necessary, reduces running costs. Thermostats can be of two types— mechanical and electrical/electronic.

Mechanical thermostats are found in ovens, irons, kettles, central heating systems etc. Most mechanical thermostats use bimetallic strips. A bimetallic strip consists of strips of iron and brass fixed together. When metals are heated they expand. However, different metals expand by different amounts. Brass expands much more than iron. When the bimetallic strip is heated it bends (Fig. 3). When the strip bends it breaks the circuit and cuts off the heater.

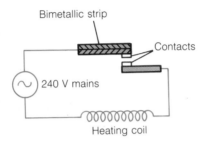

Fig. 3 A bimetallic strip

Electronic control systems

Many electronic circuits have control systems which can include both positive and negative feedback mechanisms. Electronics deals with the study of switching devices which require electric currents to make them work.

In electronics we frequently use **digital systems**. The voltage in a normal electrical circuit can be varied. In a digital system only two possibilities exist:
(a) logic level 1 i.e. ON
(b) logic level 0 i.e. OFF

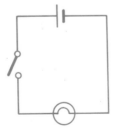

Fig. 4 A simple circuit

Consider the simple circuit in Fig. 4, consisting of a battery, bulb and switch. There are two possibilities here.

Switch	Lamp
0 (off)	0 (off)
1 (on)	1 (on)

Table 1

Table 1 is called a **truth table** and summarizes the possibilities that exist in this simple circuit.

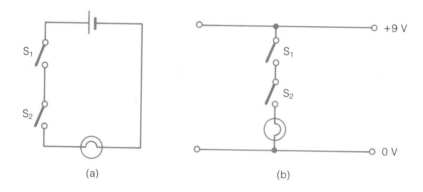

(a)   (b)

Fig. 5 A more complicated system

In Fig. 5(a) there is a more complicated system with two switches, labelled S_1 and S_2, and one bulb. There is an alternative way of representing it, shown in Fig. 5(b), which leaves out the battery and uses two **voltage lines** (or **rails**). The truth table for this is shown in Table 2.

Switch		Bulb
S_1	S_2	
0	0	0
1	0	0
0	1	0
1	1	1

Table 2

This truth table summarizes all of the possibilities. The bulb will only light if both switches are on.

Electronic devices

Table 3 contains information about common devices used in electronics.

Light-dependent resistors (LDR)
These are dimmer switches controlled by light. In strong light the LDR allows current to flow through it. In the dark very little current flows.

Light-emitting diode (LED)
Current flowing through the LED will make it light up providing the current flows in one direction. LEDs use less current and last longer than ordinary bulbs.

or

Thermistors
These are heat-sensitive resistors. They conduct electricity better when hot.

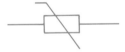

Reed switches
These are switches controlled by magnetism. In a glass tube there are two iron strips which are not in contact. When a magnet is brought close magnetism is induced. The two iron strips are attracted and the switch is closed.

Transistors
These have three connections. The third connection acts as a switch for the other two. If no current flows into the third leg (called the **base**) no current flows between the other two.

Table 3

Logic gates

These are switches which only allow an output signal in response to certain input situations. They are called **gates** because they can be *open* (logic 1) or *closed* (logic 0). Common logic gates are summarized in Table 4.

Gate	Truth table	Comments
NOT 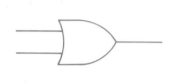	Input / Output: 0 → 1, 1 → 0	Sometimes called an inverter.
OR 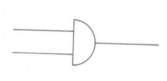	Inputs A,B / Output: 0 0 → 0, 0 1 → 1, 1 0 → 1, 1 1 → 1	Output is high if either input is high.
AND 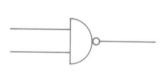	Inputs A,B / Output: 0 0 → 0, 0 1 → 0, 1 0 → 0, 1 1 → 1	Output is high if both inputs are high.
NAND 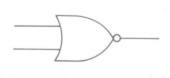	Inputs A,B / Output: 0 0 → 1, 0 1 → 1, 1 0 → 1, 1 1 → 0	Opposite of AND gate.

NOT

Input	Output
0	1
1	0

OR

Inputs		Output
A	B	
0	0	0
0	1	1
1	0	1
1	1	1

AND

Inputs		Output
A	B	
0	0	0
0	1	0
1	0	0
1	1	1

NAND

Inputs		Output
A	B	
0	0	1
0	1	1
1	0	1
1	1	0

NOR

Inputs		Output
A	B	
0	0	1
0	1	0
1	0	0
1	1	0

Opposite of OR gate. Output high if neither A nor B is high.

Table 4

Fig. 6 shows a model of a circuit which could control street lights. The bulb (representing the street light) is turned on when the light dims. The NOT switch activates the transistor when the input is turned off.

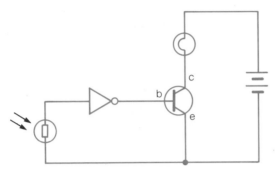

Fig. 6 A model of a circuit

There are many similar examples of electronic control mechanisms.

Summary

Many systems have to be kept stable or in equilibrium. They are controlled by a process called homeostasis. A control system has a **sensor** or **receptor**, a **control mechanism** and an **effector**. Communication between these is called **feedback** and this can be positive or negative.

The **hypothalmus** in the brain controls temperature inside the human body. If the blood is too warm or too cool steps are taken to correct the condition.

The **kidneys** control the amount of water leaving the body and maintain the correct water balance. **Reflex actions** occur automatically and without thought. Impulses from the nerve endings in the skin of the fingers (receptors) send messages to the spinal cord (control mechanism). The nerve fibres then carry a message to the muscle (effector) which acts as the effector and contracts the muscle moving the finger.

A thermostat maintains a steady temperature, switching off the heater when necessary. Most mechanical thermostats use a bimetallic strip consisting of strips of iron and brass welded together. When metals are heated they expand by different amounts and the strip bends, breaking the circuit.

Electronics is about switching. Electronic circuits make good control devices.

Revision questions

1 Fig. 7 shows a fire alarm system containing a bimetallic strip.
(a) Explain how the system would work in the event of a fire.
(b) If the wiring of the circuit burns out during the fire, is the alarm set off? Is this a disadvantage of this type of alarm system?
(c) Devise a fire alarm system based upon three thermistors in different parts of a factory such that the bell will ring if any of the thermistors record a rise in temperature.

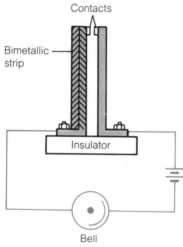

Fig. 7 A fire alarm system

2 Fig. 8 consists of a circuit with two switches S_1 and S_2.
(a) Complete the truth table, Table 5.

Input		Output
S_1	S_2	
0	0	0
0	1	
1	0	
1	1	

Table 5

(b) What logic gate is indicated by this table?
(c) Draw a symbol for this logic gate.

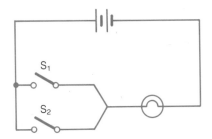

Fig. 8 A circuit (question 2)

7 The human body

Aims of the chapter

After reading this chapter you should:
1 Know that the human body is made up of cells and be familiar with the structure of a simple animal cell.
2 Know that groups of cells are called tissues and groups of tissues are called organs.
3 Know the seven main organ systems in the human body.
4 Be able to describe simply the working of the circulatory system including the function of the heart as a pump.
5 Be able to describe the respiratory system.
6 Know the essential ingredients of a healthy diet.
7 Be able to describe the digestive system.
8 Be able to describe simply the excretory system and be able to distinguish excretion and egestion.
9 Know the main uses of the human skeleton and describe main features of the skeleton.

Cells

The human body is made up from over 50 million tiny **cells** which are the building blocks from which the body is made up. Cells have different purposes in the body. Every cell, apart from a red blood cell, has a **nucleus** which controls the action of the cell. It also stores genetic information. The nucleus of the cell is surrounded by **cytoplasm** and the whole is surrounded by a **cell membrane**. Fig. 1 shows the structure of a simple cell.

Cells are usually grouped together to form **tissues**, where they work together. Tissues themselves group together to form **organs**. The organs together work to form seven main systems in the body.
1 The **circulatory** system
2 The **respiratory** system
3 The **digestive** system
4 The **excretory** system
5 The **skeletal** system
6 The **nervous** system
7 The **reproductive** system
This chapter deals with some of these organ systems.

The circulatory system

Blood is circulated around the human body. The heart acts as a pump, pumping blood from the heart in tubes called **arteries**. The blood returns to the heart in tubes called **veins**. Between the arteries and the veins, the blood passes through fine tubes called **capillaries**. Fig. 2 summarizes the circulation of the blood.

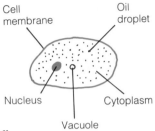

Fig. 1 A simple cell

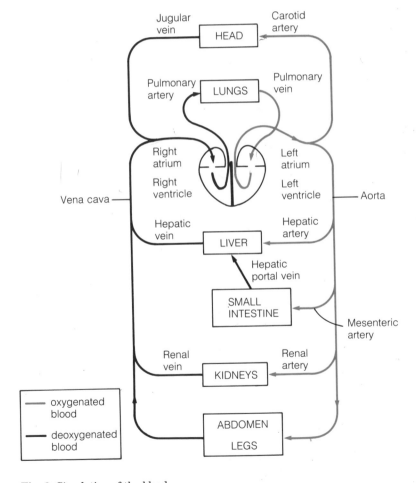

Fig. 2 Circulation of the blood

A human body contains about 25 million red blood corpuscles and about 20 million white blood corpuscles. The red blood corpuscles carry oxygen from the capillaries in the lungs to the other body cells. The red corpuscles contain haemoglobin. The white corpuscles are larger than the red blood corpuscles and protect the body against disease. The blood also contains small cell fragments called **platelets**, which help in blood clotting, and **plasma**. This contains water, mineral salts, vitamins, dissolved carbon dioxide, urea, dissolved food and hormones. It transports these substances around the body and distributes heat energy.

The heart is essentially two pumps working side by side. Fig. 3 shows a diagram of the heart. The **right atrium** takes in blood which has been around the body. The **right ventricle** pumps blood to the lungs via the pulmonary artery. The **left atrium** takes blood, rich in oxygen, from the lungs via the pulmonary vein. The **left ventricle** pumps blood, under pressure, around the body.

The valves between the atria and ventricles close when the ventricles are pumping to prevent blood being forced back into the atria.

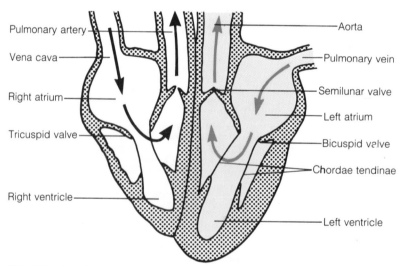

Fig. 3 The heart

If the arteries become narrowed as a result of smoking, saturated fat in the diet, stress, etc. the heart has to work harder to push the blood around the body. This causes a condition called **high blood pressure**. If food and oxygen cannot get to the heart muscles through the coronary arteries, a heart attack takes place.

The respiratory system

This is the system in the body which transports oxygen to the muscles, releases the energy by oxidation and transports the carbon dioxide from the muscles.

There are two sorts of respiration which take place in the human body—**aerobic respiration and anaerobic respiration**.

Aerobic respiration requires oxygen. It produces more energy than anaerobic respiration as the food (the fuel) is completely burnt.

Glucose + Oxygen → Carbon dioxide + Water + Energy

Anaerobic respiration takes place without oxygen and releases less oxygen. It occurs in muscles when there is less oxygen, e.g. in a strenuous race. Lactic acid is produced.

Glucose → Lactic acid + Energy

In a 100 m race an athlete builds up about 40 g of lactic acid because oxygen is used up faster than the body can take it in. At the end of the race the athlete has to breathe deeply to repay the 'oxygen debt'. A marathon runner does not build up an oxygen debt but aims to use up oxygen at the rate at which it is taken into the body.

Fig. 4 shows the human respiratory system.

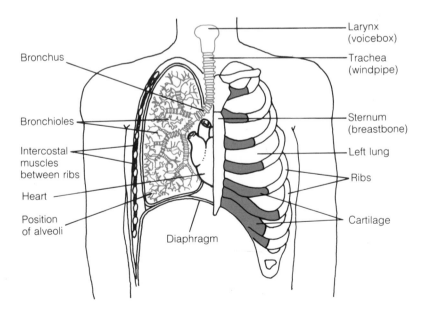

Fig. 4 The human respiratory system

Air enters the **lungs**, which consist of branched tubes, which end in millions of tiny sacs called **alveoli** (Fig. 5). The walls of the alveoli are very thin and there is a very large surface area within the alveoli. Oxygen can diffuse through the alveolus into the blood from the heart, and carbon dioxide can diffuse from the blood into the alveolus. The blood, rich in oxygen, is then returned to the heart. The blood transports oxygen to the muscles and carbon dioxide back from the muscles.

Exercise makes us breathe more quickly and more oxygen is drawn into the lungs. Smoking, air pollution and disease (bronchitis) can affect the working of the respiratory system.

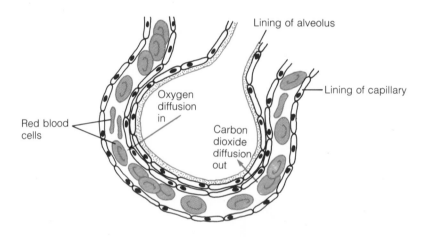

Fig. 5 An alveolus

The digestive system

Digestion is the breaking down of large insoluble food molecules into small molecules which the body can use. The digestive process involves:

1 A mechanical breaking down of the food, e.g. by chewing. This provides a larger surface area for chemical action.

2 A chemical breaking down using enzymes and acid.

Table 1 summarizes the chemical changes which take place.

Food	Enzymes	Enzymes from	Products
Proteins	proteases	stomach, pancreas, small intestine	amino acids
Carbohydrates	amylases	mouth, pancreas, small intestine	simple sugars
Fats	lipases	pancreas, small intestine	glycerol, fatty acids

Table 1

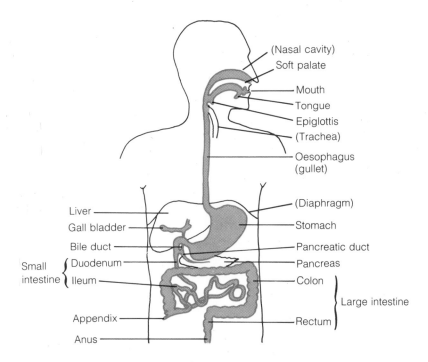

Fig. 6 The digestive system

Fig. 6 shows the digestive system. Digestion begins in the mouth where mechanical breaking down of the food occurs. The food is mixed with **saliva**, which contains the enzyme **amylase**. This starts to digest the large starch molecules. The food is swallowed and reaches the stomach. The stomach contains hydrochloric acid and the enzyme **pepsin** which can digest large protein molecules.

The partly digested food is then passed into the small intestine where enzymes from the pancreas continue the digestion. The small molecules produced, (e.g. glucose, amino acids), are absorbed through the lining of the gut into the bloodstream. The blood transports these small molecules around the body. Undigested food is passed into the large intestine where water is absorbed and faeces are formed. The faeces pass out of the body through the rectum and anus.

For good health a balanced diet is essential. The amount of the different types of food required will vary according to age, occupation and life-style. The main types of food are shown in Table 2.

Type of food	Benefit to the body	Source
Carbohydrate	provides energy (includes sugar, starch)	bread, potato
Protein	provides amino acids for building and repairing the body	meat, fish, milk, cheese
Fats	for storage and energy, provides fatty acids	butter, oil
Minerals	required in small amounts for good health (e.g. iron)	fruit, green vegetables
Vitamins	required in small amounts for good health	fruit, vegetables

Table 2

It has been shown that, in addition to the types of food in Table 2, water and fibre – or roughage – are required in the diet. Fibre or roughage is not digested but helps in the production of faeces and prevents constipation.

The excretory system

Excretion is the removal of waste products from the body. Respiration produces carbon dioxide and water and these are excreted through the lungs. Excess amino acids are broken down in the liver to form urea. Urea has to be removed from the body as it would otherwise be poisonous. Urea is taken to the kidneys where it is excreted in the urine. The kidneys also adjust the amount of water and salts in the body (p. 69).

Someone who has a damaged kidney, can be connected to a kidney machine several times a week and thus can continue living fairly normally. The blood is taken from an artery, waste materials are removed by a process called **dialysis** and the blood is then returned to the body. Very serious malfunction of a kidney may require a **kidney transplant**.

Excretion should be distinguished from **egestion**. This is the discharge of undigested remains of food in the faeces.

The skeletal system

The structure of bones is called the **skeleton**. The skeleton has several uses including:
1 Supporting the body and giving it shape.
2 Protecting vital organs, e.g. the hard skull protects the brain.
3 Blood formation: certain bones produce red and white blood cells.
4 Enabling the body to move.
Fig. 7 shows the main parts of the human skeleton.

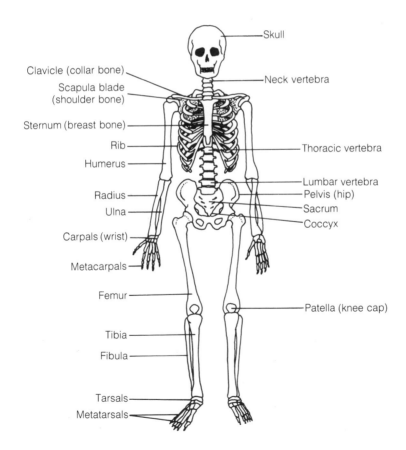

Fig. 7 The Human skeleton

The nervous system controls all of the organs in the body. Some of the functions of the nervous system are covered in Chapter 6. The reproductive system is covered in Chapter 9.

Summary

The body is made up of **cells** which have nuclei that control the action of the cells. A cell also stores genetic information. The nucleus of the cell is surrounded by **cytoplasm** and a **cell membrane**. Cells work together in **tissues** and tissues themselves group together to form **organs**. The organs together work to form seven main systems in the body.

Blood is **circulated** around the human body with the heart acting as a pump. The **respiratory system** transports oxygen to the muscles, releases the energy by oxidation and transports the carbon dioxide from the muscles.

Aerobic respiration requires oxygen. It produces more energy than anaerobic respiration as the food (the fuel) is completely burnt.

Glucose + Oxygen → Carbon dioxide + Water + Energy

Anaerobic respiration takes place without oxygen and releases less oxygen.

Glucose → Lactic acid + Energy

Smoking, air pollution and disease (bronchitis) can affect the working of the respiratory system.

Digestion is the breaking down of large insoluble food molecules into small molecules which the body can use. **Excretion** is the removal of waste products from the body.

The structure of human bones is called the skeleton. The skeleton has several uses including:
1 Supporting the body.
2 Protecting vital organs.
3 Blood formation.
4 Enabling the body to move.

The nervous system controls all of the organs in the body.

Revision questions

1 Fig. 8 shows diagrams of the cross-sections of an artery, a vein and capillary drawn to the same scale.
Which one:
(a) has the thinnest wall?
(b) has the largest diameter?
(c) is made to resist the highest pressures?

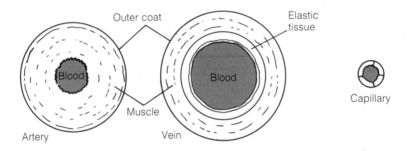

Fig. 8 Cross-sections of an artery, a vein and a capillary

2 Table 3 gives the composition of two different brands of fruit yoghurt.

per 100 g	Brand X	Brand Y
Energy value	150 kJ	480 kJ
Protein	4.5 g	4.0 g
Fat	0.3 g	2.4 g
Carbohydrate	5.2 g	18.4 g
Additives	preservative, artificial sweetener	preservative

Table 3

(a) Which brand of yoghurt would be more suitable as part of a slimmer's diet? Explain your reasoning.
(b) Brand Y contains no artificial sweetener. What do you think sweetens this brand of yoghurt?
(c) What method of storage would you recommend if these yoghurts did not contain preservative?
(d) Calculate the masses of protein, fat and carbohydrate in one 125 g tub of Brand Y.

3 Fig. 9 contains a simplified diagram of the heart, lungs and circulation system. The arrows show the direction of circulation of the blood.
(a) Identify A, B and C.
(b) Explain how the heart acts as a double pump to circulate blood around the body and also to the lungs.
(c) Many people die each year of heart disease.
(i) How can exercise and a healthy diet help to reduce the risk of heart disease?
(ii) What are the possible effects of smoking on health?

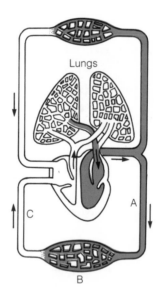

Fig. 9 Heart, lungs and circulation

Aims of the chapter

After reading this chapter you should:
1 Be able to distinguish asexual and sexual reproduction.
2 Know the meaning of mitosis and meiosis.
3 Be able to describe the importance of chromosomes.
4 Describe the role of sex chromosomes in sex determination.
5 Be able to describe sexual reproduction in humans.
6 Be able to predict the offspring expected of certain parents.
7 Know the meaning of continuous variation, discontinuous variation, mutation and natural selection.

Introduction

The cells in the human body contain nuclei. These nuclei contain **chromosomes** which store **genetic information** about the cells. This genetic information is passed on when new cells are produced. The genetic information is stored on threads of DNA by the **genes**. In a human body each cell contains twenty-three pairs of chromosomes. Twenty-two pairs are ordinary pairs and the other pair are the sex chromosomes which determine the sex of the person. If these sex chromosomes are alike (known as **XX**) the sex is female and if they are different (known as **XY**) the sex is male.

Reproduction

In Chapter 7 the reproductive system was listed as one of the seven organ systems of the human body. **Reproduction** is the making of new organisms similar to the parent or parents. There are two main types of reproduction – asexual and sexual.

Asexual reproduction

Asexual reproduction involves only one parent. Offspring are produced which are identical to the parent. Examples of asexual reproduction include:
(a) Single cell organisms, such as amoeba and bacteria, reproduce by growing and splitting into two identical halves.
(b) Part of a plant can grow into identical plants. Stem cuttings, leaf cuttings, etc. will root and produce plants, all identical.

As the offspring are identical to the parent, it is impossible to get any variation in asexual reproduction. Also, any disease or fault in the parent will be present in the offspring.

Sexual reproduction

Sexual reproduction usually involves two parents. There are many organisms, however, called **hermaphrodites**, which have both male and female sex organs and make both male and female sex cells. They include earthworms and buttercups.

Sexual reproduction involves special cells called **gametes**. When cells divided (a process called **mitosis**) during growth or repair, they produce identical cells. Each cell contains the same number of chromosomes as the parent cell. Fig. 1 shows mitosis taking place in a cell with only four chromosomes.

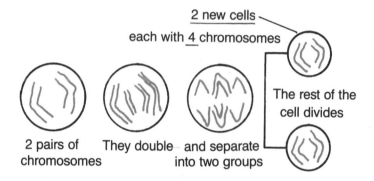

Fig. 1 Mitosis

 Gametes are not produced by mitosis but by a process called **meiosis**. Each of the chromosomes make an exact copy of itself but the parent cell divides into four new cells. Each new cell has half of the number of chromosomes of the original cell. Fig. 2 shows how this happens with a cell containing four chromosomes.

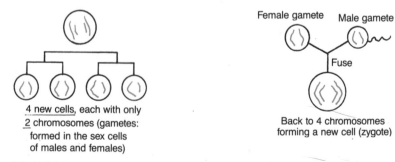

Fig. 2 Meiosis   **Fig. 3** Forming a zygote

The male and female gametes fuse together during **fertilization** to produce a new cell (or **zygote**) which has characteristics of both parents and develops into the **embryo**. This is summarized in Fig. 3.

Human reproduction

The man produces the male gametes (called the **sperm**) in the testis.
The woman produces the female gametes (called the **egg**) in the ovary.
Figs. 4 and 5 show the main parts of the reproductive systems of male
and female.

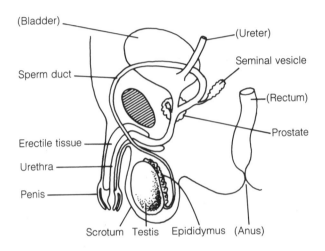

Fig. 4 The male reproductive system

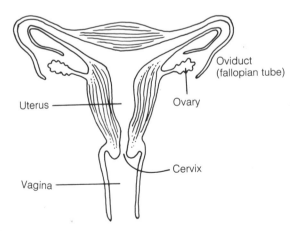

Fig. 5 The female reproductive system

During sexual intercourse, sperm passes from the male's body through the penis into the female's vagina. The sperm enters the uterus and travels along the **fallopian tubes**. If there is an egg in the fallopian tubes fertilization may take place. The fertilized egg travels to the **uterus** and beds itself in the lining. There the embryo develops and after nine months (called pregnancy or **gestation**) the baby is born, through the vagina. In contrast to many young animals, the newborn baby still needs a great deal of parental care and attention.

If fertilization does not take place, the uterus lining breaks down and is lost as part of the monthly **menstrual cycle**.

Identical twins are formed if the fertilized egg divides into two parts and each part develops into a baby. They both have the same genes and are either both male or both female. Non-identical twins are formed when two eggs are released from the ovary and both are fertilized. They do not have the same genes and can be: both male; both female; or one male and one female.

Genes

The instructions carried by a chromosome for a particular characteristic, such as eye colour, blood group etc., are called a **gene**. Every human being has two copies of each gene in every normal body cell, one in each chromosome. One gene comes from the father and one from the mother.

Genes can be **dominant** or **recessive**. A dominant gene is one whose effect is shown when there is another gene present. The recessive gene is the one whose effect is not shown. For example, if someone has genes for blue and brown eyes, their eyes will be brown. Brown is the dominant gene and blue is the recessive gene.

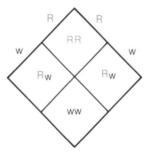

Fig. 6 Dominant and recessive genes

Fig. 6 shows two generations of breeding of plants where two colours are possible – red and white. The red gene, shown by **R**, is dominant and the white gene, shown by **w**, is recessive. The first generation is called the **F_1 hybrid** and the second generation is called the **F_2 hybrid**. You will perhaps see these terms on seed packets. You will notice that the recessive gene does not show itself in the F_1 hybrid but it does in the F_2 hybrid.

The science of genetics owes much to the work of the Austrian monk, Gregor Mendel.

Mutations

The copying of chromosomes by mitosis or meiosis is very complicated and mistakes can occur. These mistakes are called **mutations**. Mutations can be caused by radiation, X-rays and chemicals such as some drugs.

Down's syndrome is caused by mutation where the child has an extra chromosome. This occurs most frequently when the mother is older and cell division to produce eggs has not occurred properly because of ageing.

Variation

You will know that even within the same family there are variations. These are caused by new genes formed by mutation and different mixes of genes. There are two types of variation:

1 *Discontinuous variation*
This enables us to separate the population into different clearly distinguished groups e.g. by blood groups.

2 *Continuous variation*
Here clearly distinguished groups cannot be found. Height and weight are good examples. Fig. 7 shows the kind of variation which could be seen in the height of a sample of men. Genetics have some bearing but environmental factors are also important.

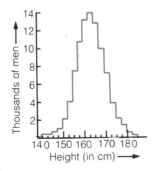

Fig. 7 Variation

Natural selection

Charles Darwin proposed the idea of natural selection after a great deal of observation of the living world. Having one form of a gene may give the organism an advantage over organisms with the other form of the gene.

Moths are eaten by birds. Light-coloured moths on light backgrounds have a better chance of survival than dark moths on light backgrounds. The light-coloured moths survive to breed and so light moths predominate.

Scientists now understand genetics and are able to carry out selective breeding of certain species. This is called **artificial selection**.

K ▶

Summary

The nucleus of a cell contains **chromosomes**. In a human body each cell contains twenty-three pairs of chromosomes. Twenty-two pairs are ordinary and the other pair are the sex chromosomes. If these chromosomes are alike (**XX**) the sex is male and if they are different (**XY**) the sex is female.

Reproduction is the making of new organisms similar to the parent or parents. **Asexual** reproduction involves only one parent and produces offspring which are identical to the parent. **Sexual** reproduction usually involves two parents and special cells called **gametes**. When cells divide (**mitosis**) they produce idential cells. Gametes, however, are produced by **meiosis**. The male and female gametes fuse together during fertilization to produce a new cell (**zygote**) which has characteristics of both parents and develops into the **embryo**.

During sexual intercourse sperm passes from the male's body through the penis into the female's vagina. If there is an egg in the **fallopian tubes** fertilization may take place.

The instructions carried by a chromosome for a particular characteristic, such as eye colour, blood group, etc., are called a **gene**. Every human being has two copies of each gene in every normal body cell, one in each chromosome. One gene comes from the father and one from the mother.

Genes can be **dominant** or **recessive**. A dominant gene is one whose effect is shown when there is another gene present. The recessive gene is the one whose effect is not shown.

Mistakes can occur in the copying of chromosomes and aberrations called **mutations** may occur. Mutations can be caused by radiation, X-rays and chemicals such as some drugs.

There are two types of variation – **discontinuous** and **continuous** variation.

Revision questions

1 Red and white flowered plants were crossed.

Red-flowered plant × White-flowered plant

  Rr   **rr**

(a) What gametes are formed by the red-flowered plant and the white-flowered plant?

(b) Which gene is dominant and which is recessive?

(c) What offspring would be formed from the cross? Show your working.

(d) What colour mixture would you expect from 100 plants produced by this cross?

2 Light-coloured moths have an advantage over dark-coloured moths when viewed against light backgrounds. What difference would you expect if the moths lived in an area where buildings were blackened by air pollution?

3 Table 1 shows information about two organisms which are similar in appearance.

	Honey-bee	Hover-fly
Body	3 segments	3 segments
Legs	3 pairs	3 pairs
Wings	2 pairs	1 pair
Colour	yellow and black stripes	yellow and black stripes
Length	1.5 cm	2 cm
Sting	yes	no

Table 1

(a) Which of the organisms is larger?

(b) Apart from size, give one difference between the two.

(c) A predator will not eat either of these organisms, even though the hover-fly is harmless.

(i) Explain the reason for the predator's behaviour.

(ii) Explain how genetic mutations in the ancestors of the hover-fly account for the similarity between the two organisms.

9 Ecology

Aims of the chapter

After reading this chapter you should:
1 Know the meaning of the terms ecology, ecosystem, biotic and abiotic.
2 Be able to define and give examples of producers, consumers, decomposers, food chains and food webs.
3 Be able to draw simple food chains to show feeding relationships.
4 Be able to interpret a food web and predict the effects of the death of some of the organisms.
5 Be able to describe and explain the pyramids of numbers and biomass.
6 Be able to identify carbon, nitrogen and water as the basic raw materials needed by living organisms.
7 Be able to describe the processes involved and the importance of carbon, nitrogen and water cycles.

Introduction

Ecology is the study of the relationships between living and non-living things in the environment. The conditions in a habitat are either **biotic** or **abiotic**. A biotic factor is, for example, what an organism eats. Abiotic factors are light, temperature, soil conditions, etc. The abiotic and biotic factors make up what we call the **ecosystem**. An ecosystem consists of the community of organisms interacting with the environment in the **habitat**.

Feeding relationships

Organisms in a habitat are interrelated because of how they feed and how their dead remains are decayed. Organisms can be divided into **producers** and **consumers**.

Producers are green plants which change light energy to trapped chemical energy by **photosynthesis**. Examples are grass on land and duckweed in water.

Consumers are animals which depend upon plants for the food they need. Consumers can be divided into primary, secondary and tertiary consumers. Primary consumers (or **herbivores**) feed on plants. Secondary consumers feed on animals which have eaten plants. Tertiary consumers feed on secondary consumers. Secondary and tertiary consumers are also called **carnivores**.

For example, in Fig. 1 we see four organisms. The cabbages are producers. The slugs, which feed on the cabbages, are called primary consumers. The pigeons, which feed on the slugs, are secondary consumers. The human, who feeds on the pigeon, is the tertiary consumer. This relationship can be summarized by a **food chain**.

Cabbage → Slug → Pigeon → Human

Fig. 1 Producers and consumers

All food chains begin with a producer.

The slug in the example is the **prey** of the pigeon and the pigeon is the **predator** of the slug. However, the pigeon can become the prey for the human.

It is obvious that the diet of an organism is more complicated than can be shown by a simple chain. The complicated relationships between organisms can be shown by a food web. Fig. 2 shows a food web.

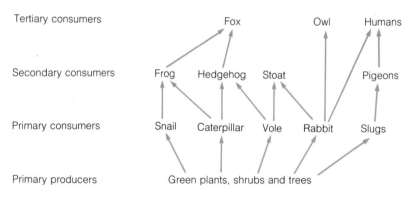

Fig. 2 A food web

When plants and animals die, all of the nutrients stored in the body are recycled by **decomposers,** such as bacteria and fungi. These organisms break down dead animals and plants and release nitrogen into the soil.

Pyramids

Primary consumers (e.g. slugs) eat producers (e.g. cabbage). Only about 10 per cent of the trapped energy in the cabbage becomes part of the slug's body. When the slugs are eaten by pigeons only 10 per cent of the energy in the food becomes part of the pigeon's body. The further up the chain we go less and less energy is passed along the chain. This leads to:

1 Fewer organisms being supported as we go along the food chain. This is summarized in Fig. 3 and is called the **pyramid of numbers**.
2 Smaller total body mass (called **biomass**) of organisms as we go along the food chain. The mass of cabbages is greater than the mass of slugs which is greater than the mass of pigeons. This is called the **pyramid of biomass**.

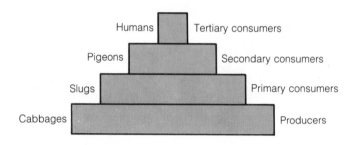

Fig. 3 The pyramid of numbers

Growth of populations

You can estimate the population of a particular species in a given area by:
1 Taking a given area, perhaps 0.25 m², and counting all of the species in that area. Repeat until you have taken the results ten times. Then calculate the average result. Use this to calculate the population in the whole area.
2 Capturing, counting and marking a number of animals. Then releasing them and recapturing them later. The total population can be calculated using the formula:

$$\text{Total population} = \frac{\text{No. in 1st sample} \times \text{No. in 2nd sample}}{\text{No. of marked animals recaptured}}$$

When a new species moves into a new area, the growth of population is slow initially. Then it grows very quickly. When the population reaches a certain level, determined by the resources available, the population is stabilized. This is summarized by Fig. 4.

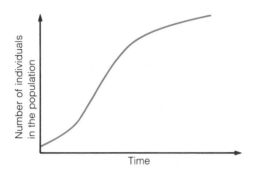

Fig. 4 Stabilization of population

Competition of species

Often the population of a particular species is determined by other species which are in competition. Fig. 5 shows the population of rabbits and foxes during the year. Notice that a growth of fox population follows a growth of rabbit population. The fox is the predator and the rabbit is the prey.

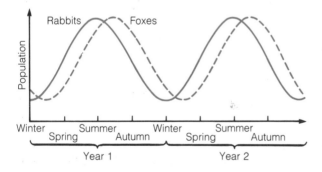

Fig. 5 Rabbits and foxes

Nutrient species

Nitrogen, carbon and water are recycled in nature. When organisms die, or when they release waste products, they are decomposed and the raw materials are released and can be used again. Fig. 6 shows the nitrogen cycle which summarizes the ways nitrogen is added and removed from the soil. When plants are growing they remove nutrients, especially nitrogen, from the soil. If the land is to remain fertile this nitrogen has to be replaced. It can be replaced naturally during thunderstorms and when plants and animals die and decay. Certain plants, such as clover, peas and beans, are able to absorb nitrogen directly from the air and fix it in the soil, as nitrates.

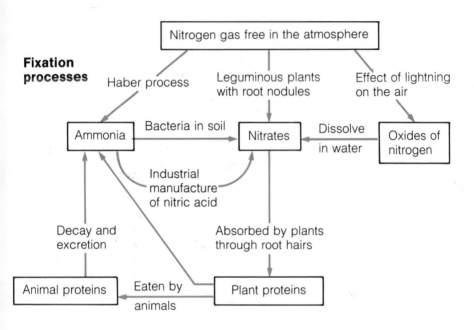

Fig. 6 The nitrogen cycle

Nitrogen in the form of nitrates can be washed out of the soil into rivers and lakes. High levels of nitrates in drinking water can cause health problems. Nitrates in water can cause algae to form. This blocks out sunlight. When the algae decay, oxygen is removed from the water.

    Fig. 7 summarizes the **carbon cycle**. Photosynthesis by plants ensures that the percentages of various gases in the air remain fairly constant.

    Fig. 8 summarizes the **water cycle**. The water in the oceans is continuously evaporated by the heat of the Sun. The vapour condenses to form clouds. When the clouds are cooled the water vapour turns to rain. Some of the rain returns to the sea via rivers. More of the water returns to the atmosphere by evaporation from the leaves of green plants (called **transpiration**).

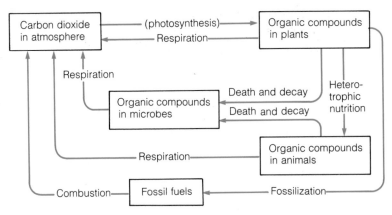

Fig. 7 The carbon cycle

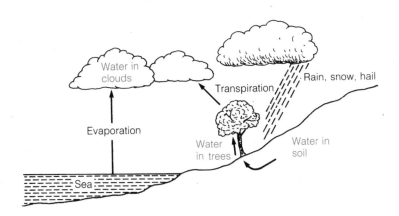

Fig. 8 The water cycle

Summary

An **ecosystem** consists of the community of organisms interacting with the environment in the **habitat**. The conditions in a habitat are either **biotic** or **abiotic**. Organisms in a habitat are interrelated and can be divided into **producers** and **consumers**.

Producers are green plants which change light energy to trapped chemical energy by **photosynthesis**. Consumers are animals which depend upon plants for food. They can be primary, secondary or tertiary consumers. The relationship between these organisms can be shown in a **food chain**. More complicated relationships are shown in a **food web**.

When plants and animals die, all of the nutrients stored in the body are recycled by decomposers which break down the dead animals and plants and release nitrogen into the soil.

At every stage in the food chain only about 10 per cent of the energy is transferred. Often the population of a particular species is determined by other species which are in competition.

Nitrogen, carbon and water are recycled in nature. When organisms die, or when they release waste products, they are decomposed and the raw materials are released and can be used again.

Revision questions

1 Kestrels are birds of prey. In recent years numbers of kestrels have increased, especially near motorways. Explain in terms of food chains why this may be so.

2 Refer back to the food web in Fig. 2. What could be the effects on the organisms in the food web of:

(a) foxes being exterminated by farmers?

(b) rabbits being killed in large numbers by disease?

3 A scientist was attempting to find out the number of puffins on a remote island. She caught 50 puffins and ringed them. She released them and a month later went back and caught 20 puffins. Four of the puffins were ringed. Calculate the number of puffins on the island.

4 Table 1 shows animals collected in two sites:

Site A: a damp, shaded area of the garden,

Site B: a dry open pasture with a sunny position.

Animal	Number of animals at	
	A	B
Snails	55	1
Worms	20	5
Centipedes	5	1
Ants	40	25
Spiders	20	15
Beetles	20	10
Aphids	20	40

Table 1

(a) Which animals occurred in large numbers at Site B rather than Site A?

(b) Complete the pie diagram in Fig. 9, showing the distribution of animals at Site A. Each segment is 20°.

(c) Which animal is likely to be a secondary consumer? Give a reason for your answer.

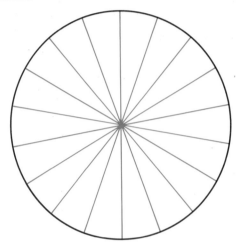

Fig. 9 A pie chart

The aims of the chapter

After reading this chapter you should:
1 Know that the Sun is a star at the centre of our solar system and that the planets orbit the Sun.
2 Be able to work out facts about the planets from information given.
3 Be able to describe the structure of the Earth.
4 Be able to describe the phases of the Moon and say why lunar and solar eclipses take place.
5 Know that the Moon and the Sun are responsible for tides on the Earth and know the different types of tide seen.
6 Know the different types of rock and understand the rock cycle.
7 Be able to describe simple features of weather forecasts.

The Sun

K

The Sun is the centre of the **solar system**. The Sun is only one of billions of stars in the Milky Way. The Sun is extremely hot and is radiating energy which is the energy which enables the Earth to function. The energy on the Sun is produced by atomic **fusion**. The Sun is essentially a mixture of hydrogen and helium gases, and the conversion of hydrogen to helium produces large amounts of energy. The temperature of the Sun at its centre has been estimated at 20 000 000 °C and at its surface about 6000 °C.

The Sun is about half-way through its life cycle of about 9600 million years. Fig. 1 shows the life cycle of a star such as the Sun.

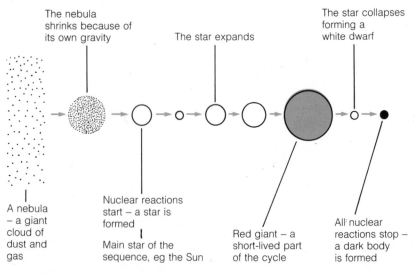

Fig. 1 The life cycle of a star

Planet	Diameter Earth = 1	Mass Earth = 1	Surface gravity Earth = 1	Density (in kg/m³)	Average distance from Sun Sun-Earth = 1	Period of orbit (in years)	Number of moons
Earth	1·00	1·00	1·00	5500	1·0	1·0	1
Jupiter	11·18	317·00	2·60	1300	5·2	11·9	16
Mars	0·53	0·10	0·40	4000	1·5	1·9	2
Mercury	0·40	0·06	0·40	5400	0·4	0·2	0
Neptune	3·93	17·20	1·20	2300	30·1	164·8	2
Pluto	0·31	0·0025	0·20	400	39·4	247·7	1
Saturn	9·42	95·00	1·10	700	9·5	29·5	15
Uranus	3·84	14·50	0·90	1600	19·2	84·0	5
Venus	0·95	0·80	0·90	5200	0·7	0·6	0

Table 1 The planets

Orbiting around the Sun are the **planets**. Table 1 gives some information about the planets. Questions at the end of the chapter will enable you to find out something about the patterns which exist.

The Earth

The Earth is one of the planets orbiting the Sun. The time taken for the Earth to orbit the Sun is about 365 days, which we call a **year**. The Earth takes 24 hours to spin on its axis and we call this time a **day**.

Fig. 2 shows the structure of the Earth. The thin layer on the surface of the Earth is called the **crust**. This consists of large **plates** of rock which are floating on the molten mantle. Fig. 3 shows how the plates are distributed over the surface of the Earth. The study of these plates and their movement is called **plate tectonics**. The movement of these plates is extremely slow, perhaps 1 to 2 cm per year. When plates collide important changes occur. It is thought that the Himalayan mountains were formed from the collision of the Indian and Eurasian plates. Some of the effects of plates moving will be met later.

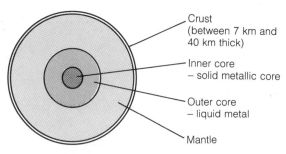

Fig. 2 The structure of the Earth

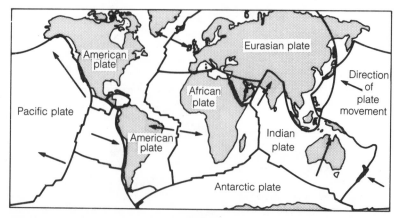

Fig. 3 The plates on the surface of the Earth

In some places the molten **magma** escapes from the Earth as lava in volcanic eruptions. The Earth's crust contains a valuable store of chemicals.

The Moon is a satellite of the Earth. It takes 28 days to orbit the Earth and this is called a **lunar month**. The view we see of the Moon varies at different times of the month, depending upon the illumination from the Sun. Fig. 4 shows the different **phases** of the Moon.

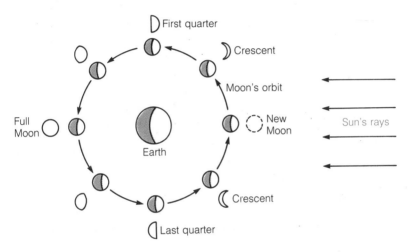

Fig. 4 Phases of the Moon

Lunar and solar eclipses

Different relative positions of the Earth and the Moon can cause blocking of light from the Sun which we call **eclipses**. There are two types of eclipses – **lunar** eclipses and **solar** eclipses. Lunar eclipses are more common than solar eclipses. Fig. 5 shows a lunar eclipse. The Earth stops light from the Sun from illuminating the Moon. There is an area of full shadow and the Moon cannot be seen from the Earth.

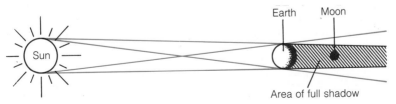

Fig. 5 A lunar eclipse

Fig. 6 shows an eclipse of the Sun (solar eclipse). The Moon passes between the Sun and the Earth and produces a shadow on the Earth.

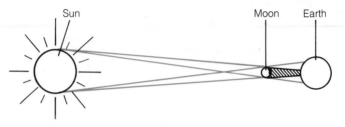

Fig. 6 A solar eclipse

The tides

The Moon exerts a gravitation pull on the water on the Earth's surface. The Moon pulls the water on the side of the Earth nearer to the Moon and produces a **high tide**. Another high tide is produced on the opposite side of the Earth. As the Earth rotates every 24 hours, there will be a high tide every 12 hours.

The Sun also exerts a gravitational pull on the water of the Earth. About twice a month the Moon and the Sun are in line and their combined gravitational pull causes a very high tide which we call a **spring tide**. These do *not* occur only in Spring.

About twice a month the gravitational pull of the Sun and the Moon are at right angles and cancel out each other. The result is a very low tide called a **neap tide**.

Rock types

There are different types of rock in the Earth.

1 *Sedimentary rocks*
The rocks in the Earth are **eroded** or broken down in many different ways. The result is a sediment made up of many different fragments. When these layers are compressed over millions of years sedimentary rocks are produced. Chalk (limestone) is a sedimentary rock.

2 *Igneous rocks*
Igneous rocks are formed when molten magma from inside the Earth is cooled. The size of the crystals produced depends upon the rate of cooling. Granite and basalt are different types of igneous rock.

3 *Metamorphic rocks*
Very high temperatures and pressures convert sedimentary rocks and igneous rocks into metamorphic rocks. Marble is a metamorphic rock formed from limestone and slate is a metamorphic rock formed from mud.

The rock cycle

Rocks are continually being broken down or **weathered**. They are then reformed into new rocks. Fig. 7 summarizes the rock cycle.

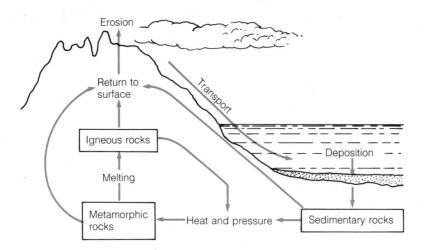

Fig. 7 The rock cycle

The weather

The Earth is surrounded with a thick layer of gases called the **atmosphere**. Changes which take place in the atmosphere are called **weather** and the study of weather is called **meteorology**.

The amount of water vapour in the atmosphere is very variable. When water evaporates the air becomes **saturated** with water vapour. As the humid air rises and cools clouds are formed. When the water vapour condenses rain is formed. Under cold conditions, water vapour condensing can cause hail or snow.

There are different types of cloud. These are shown in Table 2.

Cloud type	Height	Description
cirrus	very high	wispy white threads
cumulus	medium	white 'cotton wool'-like
nimbus	medium	dark grey
stratus	low	continous sheet of low cloud

Table 2

There are weather patterns on the Earth. In simple terms convection currents rising in the tropics and sinking at the poles produce circulating air currents. This simple pattern is confused by the spacing of land masses and the sea and the rotation of the Earth.

Convection currents in the atmosphere make areas of **low pressure** and **high pressure**. In weather forecasts pressure is given in **millibars** (mbar). Atmospheric pressure varies between about 975 mbar and 1030 mbar (about 100 kPa).

Lines on a weather chart joining up places where there is equal air pressure are called **isobars**. Areas of low pressure are called **cyclones** and are marked LOW on weather maps. High pressure areas are called **anticyclones** and are marked HIGH. In the Northern Hemisphere, winds blow in an anticlockwise direction around cyclones and in a clockwise direction around anticyclones. The closer the isobars are together the stronger will be the winds.

When cold air moves underneath an area of warm air, a **cold front** is set up. A **warm front** is formed when warm air moves above cold air. An **occluded front** is formed when a cold front catches up with a warm front. Fig. 8 shows the symbols for these fronts. As a warm front passes there will be increasing wind and cloud, light rain and a fall in pressure. Heavy rain, very strong wind and a drop in temperature accompany the passing of a cold front.

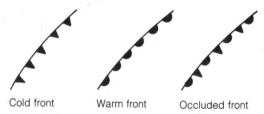

Cold front   Warm front   Occluded front

Fig. 8 Fronts

Summary

The Sun is the centre of our **solar system** and around the Sun are the **planets** orbiting. The Earth is one of the planets. The Sun is extremely hot and is radiating energy produced by **atomic fusion**. The Sun is about half-way through its **life cycle**.

The thin layer on the surface of the Earth is called the **crust** and consists of large **plates** of rock which are floating on the molten mantle. The Moon is a satellite of the Earth. It takes 28 days to orbit the Earth and this is called a **lunar month**.

Different relative positions of the Earth and the Moon can cause blocking of light from the Sun which we call **eclipses**. There are two types of eclipse – **lunar** eclipses and **solar** eclipses.

The Moon and the Sun exert gravitation pulls on the water on the Earth's surface, causing **tides**.

Sedimentary rocks, **igneous** rocks and **metamorphic** rocks are three types of rock found in the Earth. The **rock cycle** shows how these different types of rock are related.

The Earth is surrounded with a thick layer of gases called the **atmosphere**. Changes which take place in the atmosphere are called **weather** and the study of weather is called **meteorology**.

There are different types of cloud. Convection currents rising in the tropics and sinking at the poles produce circulating air currents. This simple pattern is confused by the spacing of land masses and the sea and the rotation of the Earth.

Convection currents in the atmosphere make areas of **low pressure** and **high pressure**. Lines on a weather chart joining up places where there is equal air pressure are called **isobars**. Areas of low pressure are called **cyclones** and are marked LOW on weather maps. High pressure areas are called **anticyclones** and are marked HIGH. When cold air moves underneath an area of warm air, a **cold front** is set up. A **warm front** is formed when warm air moves above cold air.

Revision questions

1 Use Table 1 to answer the following questions.
(a) Which of the planets
(i)   takes the shortest time to orbit the Sun?
(ii)   have no moons?
(iii) has the greatest density?
(iv)   has the largest diameter?
(b) Arrange the planets in order of distance from the Sun starting with the one which is closest to the Sun.
(c) How do the diameters and densities of planets close to the Sun differ from those of planets furthest from the Sun?
2 Fig. 9 shows a map where severe earthquakes have been recorded. Compare this with the distribution of plates in Fig. 3.
(a) What do you notice from these two maps?
(b) Suggest any reason for this connection.

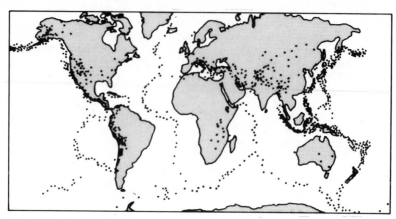

Fig. 9 Distribution of earthquakes

11 Matter and particles

Aims of the chapter

After reading this chapter you should:

1 Know that everything around us is called **matter** and can exist in three states – solid, liquid or gas.

2 Know that matter is made up of tiny particles and know how the particles are arranged and how they move in solids, liquids and gases.

3 Be able to explain properties of gases, evaporation of liquids, osmosis and dissolving in terms of a simple kinetic theory.

4 Explain the processes of distillation and fractional distillation, giving industrial examples of their use.

5 Be able to describe simple examples of **diffusion** in gases and liquids.

6 Be able to apply the knowledge that heavy particles move more slowly than lighter ones.

7 Know that an **element** is a substance which cannot be split up by chemical means and recall the symbols of common elements.

8 Be able to recall that elements are composed of atoms.

9 Know that mixtures may be separated by physical means and that they have the properties of the constituents.

10 Know that a compound has properties different from those of its constituent elements.

11 Be able to give correct names to simple compounds and list the elements present in simple compounds.

12 Be able to write the chemical formulae of simple substances, e.g. O_2, H_2, N_2, Cl_2, CO_2, NH_3, H_2O, HCl, H_2SO_4, HNO_3, CuO, $CuSO_4$, MgO, $CaCO_3$

13 Know that all atoms are made up from protons, neutrons and electrons and know the relative masses and charges of protons, neutrons and electrons.

14 Be able to work out the numbers of protons, neutrons and electrons in an atom given the mass number and atomic number.

15 Know that the protons and neutrons are tightly packed together in a positively charged nucleus and know the arrangement of electrons around the nucleus for the first 18 elements.

16 Be able to draw simple diagrams of atoms showing protons, neutrons and electrons.

17 Know that ions are formed when atoms gain or lose electrons.

18 Know the types of radiation lost during radioactive decay and the properties of each type of radiation.

19 Be able to work out the half-life of a radioactive isotope from experimental results.

20 Be able to work out the changes within the atom which accompany α and β decay.

21 Be able to state uses of radioactivity.

States of matter

In Science we are interested in all the substances in the world around us. Everything in the world around us we call **matter**.

All matter can exist in three states depending upon conditions of temperature and pressure. The three **states of matter** are **solid, liquid** and **gas**. Water, for example, can be found in three forms:

Ice solid;

Water liquid;

Steam gas.

When liquid water is heated it turns to steam at 100 °C. The water is said to be **boiling** and this temperature is called the **boiling point** of water.

When steam is cooled it turns back to water. The steam is said to be **condensing**.

When water is cooled it turns to ice at 0 °C. This is called the **freezing point** of water. At 0 °C, **melting** of ice also takes place and ice turns to liquid water. This temperature is called the **melting point** of ice.

Steam can also turn straight to ice under certain conditions. Solid ice forms inside a freezer when steam in the air is cooled rapidly. This change of state, from gas to solid, is called **sublimation**. These changes of state are summarized in Fig 1. Some of these changes require energy and others give out energy.

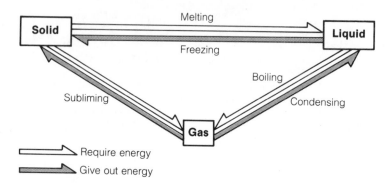

Fig. 1 Changes of state

Matter is made up of particles

A small drop of perfume will spread throughout the room. This can be explained if it is assumed that the drop of perfume is made up of millions of particles. These particles are too small to be seem even with a powerful microscope (Fig. 2).

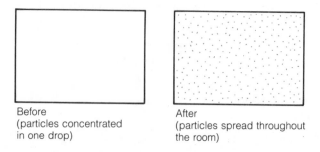

Before
(particles concentrated
in one drop)

After
(particles spread throughout
the room)

Fig. 2 Particles

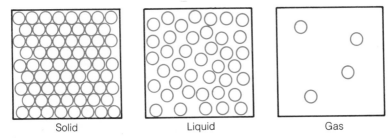

Fig. 3 Particles in solids, liquids and gases

All matter is made up from tiny particles. Fig. 3 shows simple diagrams of particles in solids, liquids and gases. These diagrams are very much simplified and it is important to remember the following points:

1 Particles are usually regularly arranged in solids and irregularly arranged in liquids and gases. A regular arrangement of particles in a solid leads to the formation of a **crystal**.

2 Particles are usually more closely packed in solids than in liquids and more closely packed in liquids than in gases.

3 Particles are constantly moving in solids, liquids and gases. The movement is greatest in a gas and least in a solid. In each case, there is no pattern to the movement. It is said to be **random** motion.

This model of how matter is made up of particles in constant motion is called the **kinetic theory**. We can use the kinetic theory to explain many of the observations which we make in the laboratory and everyday life.

Properties of gases

If some air is trapped in a bicycle pump it is easy to push in the plunger and **compress** the gas. The particles move closer together. As a result there are more collisions between the particles and the walls of the container. Moving the gas particles closer together is said to increase the gas **pressure**.

The pressure of a gas is also increased by raising the temperature. This makes the particles move faster and again there will be more collisions with the walls of the container.

Evaporation of liquids

If a saucer of water is left on a window-sill the water will slowly disappear. The water has not boiled but **evaporation** has taken place. Evaporation, like boiling, involves a change of state from liquid to gas but it is at any temperature, not necessarily the boiling point. We can explain evaporation in terms of the kinetic theory.

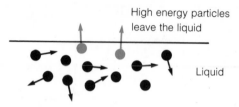

Fig. 4 Surface of a liquid

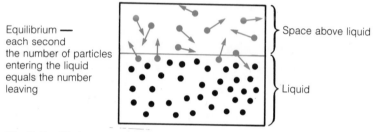

Fig. 5 Equilibrium

Fig. 4 shows the surface of the liquid. The particles in the liquid have different energies. Some fast-moving particles have enough energy to escape from the liquid. Particles above the liquid can return to the liquid. In a closed container **equilibrium** can be established (Fig. 5) where the number of particles leaving the liquid each second is the same as the number of particles entering the liquid.

The evaporation of a liquid can be speeded up by:
(a) **Draughts or blowing** across the surface of the liquid. When the particles leave the liquid they are blown away and cannot return to the liquid.
(b) **Heating.** Heating supplies energy so that more particles have enough energy to leave the liquid.
(c) **Reducing the pressure** above the liquid, which allows the particles to escape more easily from the liquid.

Dissolving

When salt is added to water, the salt disappears. We know the salt is still there because the water tastes salty! The salt is said to have **dissolved**. In this case, water is called the **solvent** and salt is called the **solute**. The resulting mixture is called a **solution**.

If you fill a beaker with water until it is almost overflowing and then sprinkle salt onto the surface of the water, the solution does not overflow when the salt dissolves. Fig. 6 shows what happens when a solid dissolves in a liquid. The particles of the solid fill in spaces between the liquid particles.

Solute particles fill gaps between solvent particles

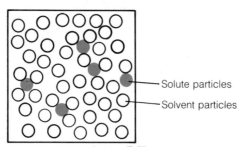

Solute particles

Solvent particles

Fig. 6 A solid dissolves in a liquid

The solute can be recovered from the solution by evaporating (or boiling) the liquid away, using the apparatus in Fig. 7.

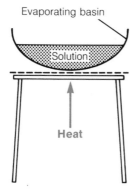

Evaporating basin

Solution

Heat

Fig. 7 Evaporation

Osmosis

A concentrated sugar solution is placed in a bag made of visking tubing. This is then placed in a beaker of water. In a short time the bag starts to swell (Fig. 8). This is due to water particles passing through the wall of the visking tubing. The process is called **osmosis**. Fig. 9 shows more clearly what is happening. The visking tubing acts as a sort of particle sieve, called a **selectively permeable membrane (SPM)**. It will allow water particles to pass through, but not the larger sugar particles. There are more water particles on the left-hand side of the membrane and so the flow of water particles from left to right is going to be greater than the movement from right to left. The net effect of the process causes the bag to swell.

Osmosis is the most important process. Water enters a plant cell through the cell membrane which acts as a SPM. The solution inside the cell is more concentrated than water outside. Water passes into the cell by osmosis.

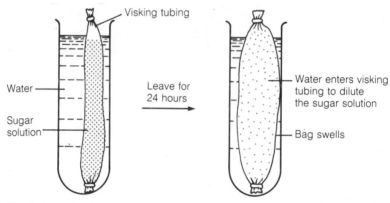

Visking tubing

Water

Sugar solution

Leave for 24 hours

Water enters visking tubing to dilute the sugar solution

Bag swells

Fig. 8 Osmosis

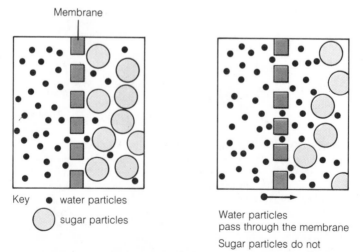

Membrane

Key   ● water particles

⬤ sugar particles

Water particles pass through the membrane

Sugar particles do not

Fig. 9 How osmosis takes place

Distillation and fractional distillation

These processes are important industrial processes, relying upon
changes of state. If a salt solution is heated, the water boils and turns
from liquid to gas (steam). On cooling, the steam condenses and water
is reformed. The process of boiling (or evaporating) followed by
condensing is called **distillation**. It can be used, for example, for
recovering pure water, called **distilled water**, from sea water.

Fig. 10 shows apparatus which can be used for distillation in the
laboratory. The salt (or other solids) remain in the flask. The
water-cooled condenser helps to condense the water produced.

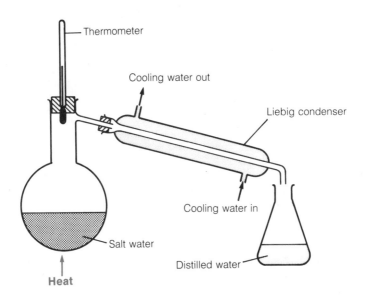

Fig. 10 Distillation

Fractional distillation is an important industrial process, used for
separating mixtures of liquids with different boiling points. The
particles of liquids with low boiling points escape from a mixture more
easily than particles of liquids with high boiling points. Fractional
distillation is used industrially:
1 To separate oxygen and nitrogen from liquid air.
2 To produce useful products such as petrol and paraffin from
petroleum.
3 To produce spirits such as whisky from solutions containing ethanol
and water.

Diffusion

Diffusion is the movement of particles of a gas or liquid to fill all of the available space.

If a drop of red bromine is put into a large gas jar, the liquid turns to a red-brown gas which fills the whole gas jar. One drop of liquid bromine contains enough bromine particles to fill the gas jar.

Diffusion also takes place in liquids but more slowly. If a purple crystal of potassium permanganate is dropped into a beaker of water, diffusion takes place. After a few hours the whole solution will be a pale pink colour. The particles in a single crystal will spread throughout the solution.

Particles diffuse at different rates

Ammonia and hydrogen chloride are both gases. They are both made up of particles. Hydrogen chloride particles are about twice as heavy as ammonia particles. When the two gases mix together a white solid, called ammonium chloride, is formed.

Different rates of diffusion can be shown in an experiment (Fig. 11). A long, dry tube is clamped horizontally. A piece of cotton wool, soaked in ammonia solution, is placed at one end of the tube. At the same time a piece of cotton wool soaked in hydrogen chloride solution is placed at the other end. The two gases move along the tube. If the two gases were to move at the same speed, they would meet and form a ring of ammonium chloride in the middle of the tube. The ring does not form in the middle, however. The position of the ring is shown in Fig. 11. The smaller ammonia particles move about twice as fast as the hydrogen chloride particles.

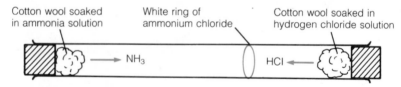

Fig. 11 Rates of diffusion

Smaller, lighter particles travel faster than, larger heavier particles.

Elements

All pure substances are made up from one or more of 105 **elements**. There are joined together in different ways to give *all* of the substances in the world around us.

Hydrogen and oxygen are two elements. When hydrogen and oxygen are combined together water is formed.

An element is a pure substance which cannot be split up into anything simpler by chemical reactions. Many of these elements are found in nature but some are made in factories.

Table 1 gives some of the common elements. For each element there is a chemical symbol which is one or two letters which are used as an abbreviation for the element.

Metals	Non-metals
Aluminium, Al	Bromine, Br
Calcium, Ca	Carbon, C
Copper, Cu	Chlorine, Cl
Iron, Fe	Fluorine, F
Lead, Pb	Helium, He
Magnesium, Mg	Hydrogen, H
Potassium, K	Iodine, I
Silver, Ag	Nitrogen, N
Sodium, Na	Oxygen, O
Zinc, Zn	Phosphorus, P
	Sulphur, S

Table 1 Common elements

Most of the known elements are solids and metals. There are only two elements which are liquid at room temperature and atmospheric pressure – bromine is a liquid non-metal and mercury is a liquid metal. The elements in the left-hand column of Table 1 are all metals. Those in the right-hand column are non-metals.

Hydrogen, helium, nitrogen, oxygen, fluorine, neon, chlorine, argon, krypton, xenon and radon are the only elements that are gases at room temperature and atmospheric pressure. All elements are made up from tiny particles called **atoms**. These atoms are so small that they cannot be seen even with a microscope.

Elements can be mixed together to form a **mixture**. For example, iron and copper powders can be mixed together to form a mixture. The mixture can be separated with a magnet. If you look carefully at the mixture with a hand lens you will be able to see pieces of iron and copper. The mixture has all of the properties of iron and copper.

Compounds

Certain mixtures of elements react together or **combine** to form **compounds**.

For example, a mixture of hydrogen and oxygen explodes and form droplets of water.

This formation of a compound from its constituent elements is sometimes called **synthesis**.

Iron(II) sulphide, the compound formed when the elements iron and sulphur combine, has entirely different properties from iron and sulphur. It is extremely difficult to get iron and sulphur back from iron(II) sulphide. The iron and sulphur atoms join together to form pairs of atoms called **molecules**. A sample of iron(II) sulphide consists of molecules: each molecule consisting of one iron atom and one sulphur atom. The synthesis of iron(II) sulphide is summarized in Fig. 12.

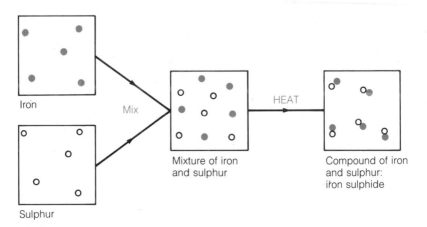

Iron

Mix

Mixture of iron and sulphur

HEAT

Compound of iron and sulphur: iron sulphide

Sulphur

Fig. 12 The synthesis of iron(II) sulphide

Elements present in compounds

You will meet only a limited number of compounds during a Science course. Often the name can tell you the elements that are present in the compound.

The chemical name will usually tell you the elements that are combined in the compound. If a compound ends in -ide, the compound contains only two elements. For example:

(a) sodium chloride   sodium and chlorine
(b) copper(II) oxide   copper and oxygen

There is one important exception to this rule. Sodium hydroxide is composed of **three** elements – sodium, oxygen and hydrogen.

If a compound ends in -ate, the compound contains oxygen. For example:

(a) calcium carbonate   calcium, carbon and oxygen
(b) copper(II) sulphate   copper, sulphur and oxygen
(c) sodium hydrogensulphate   sodium, hydrogen, sulphur and oxygen

Names such as ethanol, glucose and starch, however, give little indication of the elements present.

If you see a formula, such as K_3PO_4, you should be able to name the compound. In this case it would be potassium phosphate.

Table 2 contains a list of some of the common substances that you will use during a Science course. You should try to remember these formulae. There are rules to enable you to work out formulae but you probably will not need to be able to do this.

Oxygen	O_2	Sulphuric acid	H_2SO_4
Hydrogen	H_2	Nitric acid	HNO_3
Nitrogen	N_2	Copper(II) oxide	CuO
Chlorine	Cl_2	Copper(II) sulphate	$CuSO_4$
Carbon dioxide	CO_2	Magnesium oxide	MgO
Ammonia	NH_3	Calcium carbonate	$CaCO_3$
Water	H_2O	Magnesium chloride	$MgCl_2$
Hydrochloric acid (or hydrogen chloride)	HCl	Calcium chloride	$CaCl_2$

Table 2 Common substances

Particles in an atom

All elements are made up of tiny atoms. These atoms in turn are made up of smaller particles called **protons** (p), **neutrons** (n) and **electrons** (e).

Table 3 summarizes the masses and charges of these three particles.

Particle	Approximate mass*	Charge
Proton, p	1 u	+1
Neutron, n	1 u	0
Electron, e	negligible	−1

* u stands for an atomic mass unit. This is the unit we use for comparing the masses of atoms.

Table 3

All atoms are neutrally charged. This means that an atom contains equal numbers of protons and electrons. The number of neutrons is less important. It alters the mass but does not alter the charge.

For any atom, you will see the **atomic number** (Z) and **mass number** (A). The atomic number is the number of protons in an atom (equal also to the number of electrons). The mass number is the number of protons and neutrons in the atom.

A sodium atom has a mass number of 23 and an atomic number of 11. It contains 11 protons, 11 electrons and 12 neutrons.

Arrangement of particles in an atom

The protons and neutrons in any atom are tightly packed together in the **nucleus** of the atom. The nucleus is positively charged. The electrons move around the nucleus.

The electrons move around the nucleus in certain **energy levels**. Each energy level is able to hold up to a certain maximum number of electrons. Fig. 13 shows a simple representation of an atom.

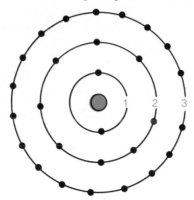

Fig. 13 A simple representation of an atom

The first energy level (labelled 1 in Fig. 13) can hold a maximum of two electrons. This energy level is filled first.

The second energy level (labelled 2) can hold up to eight electrons. It is filled after the first energy level and before the third.

There are higher energy levels which hold larger numbers of electrons.

A sodium atom has a nucleus containing 11 protons and 12 neutrons. The 11 electrons move around the nucleus with 2 electrons in the first energy level (it is then full), 8 electrons in the second energy level (again full) and 1 electron in the third energy level. The electron arrangement of a sodium atom is written down as 2, 8, 1.

Fig. 14 shows a simple representation of a sodium atom.

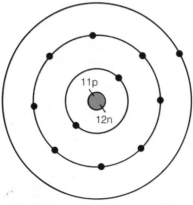

p = proton
n = neutron

Fig. 14 A sodium atom

Table 4 gives the numbers of protons, neutrons and electrons in the first 18 elements. It also gives the electron arrangement in each element.

Element	Atomic number	Mass number	Number of p	n	e	Arrangement of electrons
Hydrogen	1	1	1	0	1	1
Helium	2	4	2	2	2	2
Lithium	3	7	3	4	3	2,1
Beryllium	4	9	4	5	4	2,2
Boron	5	11	5	6	5	2,3
Carbon	6	12	6	6	6	2,4
Nitrogen	7	14	7	7	7	2,5
Oxygen	8	16	8	8	8	2,6
Fluorine	9	19	9	10	9	2,7
Neon	10	20	10	10	10	2,8
Sodium	11	23	11	12	11	2,8,1
Magnesium	12	24	12	12	12	2,8,2
Aluminium	13	27	13	14	13	2,8,3
Silicon	14	28	14	14	14	2,8,4
Phosphorus	15	31	15	16	15	2,8,5
Sulphur	16	32	16	16	16	2,8,6
Chlorine	17	35	17	18	17	2,8,7
Argon	18	40	18	22	18	2,8,8

Table 4 Numbers of protons, neutrons and electrons in the principal isotopes of the first 18 elements

Isotopes

It is possible to have different atoms of the same element containing different numbers of neutrons. The different atoms are called **isotopes**.

Chlorine, for example, has two isotopes: chlorine-35 and chlorine-37. Chlorine-35 (mass number 35, atomic number 17) contains 17 protons, 17 electrons and 18 neutrons. Chlorine-37 (mass number 37, atomic number 17) contains 17 protons, 17 electrons and 20 neutrons. Both isotopes have similar electron arrangements and hence similar chemical properties. They will have different masses and, therefore, different physical properties. If chlorine is produced in the laboratory, it is made up of 75 per cent chlorine-35 and 25 per cent chlorine-37.

Some elements, such as flourine, have only one isotope.

The **relative atomic mass** (abbreviated to RAM or A_r) of an element is based upon the average mass of all the atoms in the element (taking the isotope carbon-12 as the standard). It will not usually be an exact whole number. Approximate relative atomic masses are given in the Periodic Table (p. 134) and are often found in questions on examination papers.

Formation of ions

Atoms can gain or lose electrons. The particle produced when an atom gains or loses electrons will not contain equal numbers of protons and electrons. It will therefore be charged and is called an **ion**.

Metals tend to lose electrons and form ions with positive charge. These ions are sometimes called **cations**. Table 5 gives the electron arrangements of sodium, magnesium and aluminium atoms. It also gives the number of electrons lost by each atom when it forms an ion, the ion produced and the electron arrangement of the ion.

Atom of element	Electron arrangement	Number of electrons lost	Ion produced	Electron arrangement of ion
Sodium, Na	2,8,1,	1	Na^+	2,8
Magnesium, Mg	2,8,2	2	Mg^{2+}	2,8
Aluminium, Al	2,8,3	3	Al^{3+}	2,8

Table 5

When an atom loses one electron it forms an ion with a single positive charge. When an atom loses two electrons the ion formed has a 2+ charge. In each case, only the electrons from the highest energy level are lost. All three ions have the same electron arrangement but they are not the same because they have different numbers of protons.

Non-metals form negative ions by gaining electrons. These negative ions are sometimes called **anions**. Table 6 gives the electron arrangements of oxygen and fluorine atoms. It also gives the number of electrons gained by each atom when it forms an ion, the ion produced and the electron arrangement of the ion.

Atom of element	Electron arrangement	Number of electrons gained	Ion produced	Electron arrangement of ion
Fluorine, F	2,7	1	F^-	2,8
Oxygen, O	2,6	2	O^{2-}	2,8

Table 6

Radioactivity

The nuclei of some heavier atoms are unstable and tend to split up, with the emission of certain types of radiation and the formation of new elements. This decay is called **radioactive decay**.

It is possible for lighter atoms containing a larger proportion of neutrons than the common isotopes to undergo radioactive decay. For example, hydrogen-3 (tritium) and carbon-14 are radioactive isotopes containing more neutrons than hydrogen-1 and carbon-12 respectively.

Types of radiation emitted

The radiation emitted during radioactive decay can be of three types:

1 ∝ *(alpha) – particles*
These are positively charged particles, each of which is identical with the nucleus of a helium atom, i.e. two protons and two neutrons but no electrons. They are comparatively heavy and slow-moving and have little penetrating power. For example, they are unable to penetrate a piece of paper. They are deflected by magnetic and electrostatic fields. Because of their poor penetrating power they cannot be detected by the usual apparatus used in the laboratory.

2 β *(beta) – rays*
These are negatively charged particles. In fact, they are electrons. They have greater penetrating power than α-particles and are deflected by magnetic and electrostatic fields.

3 γ *(gamma) – rays*
These are high-energy electromagnetic waves with zero charge. They are very penetrating and are unaffected by electric and magnetic fields. Although they penetrate the detecting apparatus, they are not recorded on the normal laboratory apparatus.

Detecting radioactivity

Radioactivity was first detected when it 'fogged' photographic plates in the same way as light affects a photographic plate. This principle is still used today in taking X-ray photographs.

Today radioactivity is detected using a **Geiger counter** attached to a suitable counting tube. The tube is filled with a gas which is mainly argon. When radiation enters the tube, some of the gas atoms are ionized. The tiny electric current set up is detected on the counter.

Because there is natural radioactivity in the environment from cosmic rays entering the atmosphere, rocks (especially granite), etc., it is necessary to correct for **background radiation**. In an experiment, if the Geiger counter reading is 512 counts per second (cps) when the sample is in place but 10 cps in the absence of any radioactive sample, the corrected reading is 502 cps (i.e. 512 − 10).

Half-life

K

K

The rate of decay of a radioactive isotope is independent of temperature. The time taken for half the mass of a radioactive isotope to decay is called the **half-life** and is a characteristic of the isotope. It is the time taken for the corrected reading on the Geiger counter to fall to half of its original value.

Half-life of $^{214}_{84}$Po = 1.5×10^{-4} s

Half-life of $^{226}_{88}$Ra = 1620 years

A graph can be plotted like the one in Fig. 15, if readings are taken at intervals and then corrected for background radiation. If a convenient reading is taken (say 2000 cps) and the lines AB and BC are drawn, then the lines DE and EF can be drawn at a reading which is half of the original reading. The difference between BC and EF is called the half-life.

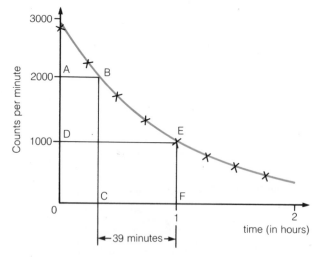

Fig. 15 Finding half-life

Changes accompanying radioactive decay

Radioactive decay can change the numbers of protons and neutrons in the nucleus of an atom.

When an isotope loses an α–particle, it loses two protons and two neutrons. For example, α–decay of uranium–238 occurs like this.

$$^{238}_{92}\text{U} \rightarrow ^{4}_{2}\text{He} + ^{234}_{90}\text{Th}$$

uranium$-238 \rightarrow \alpha-$particle $+$ thorium-234

The product of α−decay contains two fewer protons and, therefore, is two places to the left of uranium in the Periodic Table.

When an isotope undergoes β−decay, a neutron in the nucleus changes to a proton and an electron. The electron is lost as the β−particle. The product, therefore, has one more proton than the starting isotope, and is one place to the right in the Periodic Table. For example, β−decay of thorium−234 occurs like this:

$$^{234}_{92}\text{Th} \rightarrow\, ^{234}_{91}\text{Pa} + \text{electron}$$

thorium $-234 \rightarrow$ protactinium$-234 + \beta$−particle

The emission of γ-rays does not alter the number of protons or neutrons in the isotope. Gamma radiation usually accompanies other types of emission.

Uses of radioactivity

Radioactivity has a large number of uses in industry. These include:
1 Treating cancer by subjecting the patient to controlled amounts of γ− radiation from cobalt−60 or a similar source.
2 Sterilizing instruments and equipment using γ−radiation.
3 Controlling the thickness of sheets of paper, rubber, metals and plastic accurately during manufacture.
4 Controlling the filling of packets and containers.
5 Tracing the movement of a substance through a system by following the progess of a radioactive isotope, e.g. liquid through a pipe.
6 The energy produced by radioactive decay of uranium−235 (called **fission**) is used within a nuclear power station to produce electricity (see p. 8). An uncontrolled nuclear fission produces tremendous energy in an atomic bomb.
7 Irradiation of food with γ−radiation to kill bacteria and ensure that food is fit to eat. This is allowed in some countries and is used often on shellfish.
8 Carbon−14 dating is used to date ancient objects. All living things contain a small amount of carbon−14. When the organism dies the carbon−14 starts to decay (half-life 5736 years). By finding out how much carbon−14 is still present, an object can be accurately dated. This was used recently to date the Turin Shroud.

The uses of a radioactive isotope depends upon its half-life. If the half-life is too short or too long it can have little practical application.

Summary

All substances can exist in three states of matter depending upon temperature and pressure. These are **solid**, **liquid** and **gas**. The change from solid to liquid is called **melting**. **Boiling** is the change from liquid to gas at a particular temperature, called the **boiling point**. The same change, which takes place more slowly at lower temperatures, is called **evaporation**. **Freezing** is the change from liquid to solid. Missing out the liquid stage is called **sublimation**.

All matter is made up from tiny **particles**. In a solid, they are generally closely packed together and are only moving slightly. In a liquid, the particles are slightly further apart and are moving slightly more than in the solid. The particles in a gas are widely spaced, irregularly arranged and moving rapidly in all directions. The collisions of the particles with the walls of the container leads to **gas pressure**. The movement of particles in solid, liquids and gases is random.

Dissolving involves the breaking down of the arrangement of particles in the solute. These particles fill gaps between the solvent particles. Evaporation involves the escape of fast-moving particles from the surface of the liquid.

Osmosis is the passage of solvent particles (e.g. water) through a selectively permeable membrane (SPM). Larger solute molecules (e.g. sugar) will not pass through the SPM.

Distillation is used to separate a solvent from a solution, e.g. water from salt solutions. **Fractional distillation** is used to separate mixtures of liquids with different boiling points.

Diffusion is the movement of particles to fill all of the available space. It takes place rapidly with gases and slowly with liquids. Small, light particles diffuse faster than larger, heavier particles.

All substances are made up from a number of simple **elements**. An element is a pure substance which cannot be split up by chemical reactions. Elements are made up from tiny particles called **atoms**.

Elements can be mixed together to form a **mixture**. The properties of a mixture are the same as the properties of the elements that make it up. The elements can be separated from the mixture.

Elements can combine together to form **compounds**. This is called **synthesis**. When a compound forms, the atoms of the different elements join together to form small **molecules**. It is difficult to get the elements back from a compound.

Atoms are made up from **protons**, **neutrons** and **electrons**. All atoms are neutral and contain equal numbers of protons and electrons. The **atomic number** (Z) is the number of protons (and also electrons) in an atom. The **mass number** (A) is the number of protons plus neutrons in an atom.

In any atom the protons and neutrons are packed in the **nucleus**. Electrons move around the nucleus in energy levels. Atoms of the same element containing different numbers of neutrons are called **isotopes**. When an atom gains or loses electrons it forms an **ion**.

Radioactive materials can emit α−, β− or γ− radiation. The rate of this emission or decay does not depend upon temperature. The time taken for half of a radioactive sample to decay is called its **half-life**. Emission of α− and β− particles changes the number of protons and neutrons in an atom, and therefore changes the isotope.

Radioactive isotopes have a wide range of uses. Apart from the production of atomic bombs and the generation of electricity in a nuclear power station, there are many other industrial, medical and scientific uses.

Revision questions

1 Fig. 16 shows a beaker containing 20 cm³ of a liquid called ether. The beaker is standing on a wet block of wood.

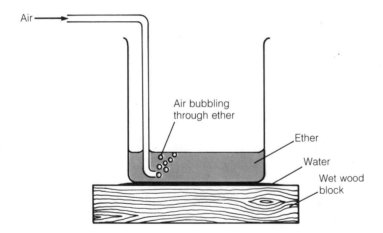

Fig. 16

Air is blown through the ether for a few minutes. The volume of ether remaining is 10 cm³ and the water under the beaker has frozen.
(a) Explain the reason for the reduction in the volume of ether in the beaker.
(b) Why is the water under the beaker frozen?
(c) There is a smell of ether throughout the room. What name is given to the process which spreads the smell throughout the room?

2 Using the information in Table 4 (on p. 125), draw simple diagrams showing arrangements of protons, neutrons and electrons in:
(a) a carbon atom
(b) a neon atom
(c) two isotopes of chlorine.
3 Measurements were made with a Geiger counter and tube to find the half-life of a radioactive isotope **X**. The results obtained are shown in Table 7.

Time in minutes	0	10	20	30	40	50	60	70
Count rate (cps)	650	520	416	333	300	213	170	136

All results have been corrected for background radiation
Table 7

(a) Plot these results on the graph labelled Fig. 17.
(b) Which result appears to be incorrect?
(c) Draw a smooth curve through the other points.
(d) What count rate would you expect after 25 minutes?
(e) What is the half-life of the isotope **X**? Explain how you arrived at this answer.

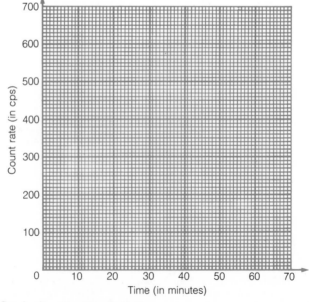

Fig. 17 Graph of count rate against time

Aims of the chapter

After reading through this chapter you should:

1 Be able to describe the structure of the Periodic Table.

2 Know the elements in the same vertical column or group have similar properties.

3 Be able to describe the changes in metallic character across a period and down a group.

4 Know the relationship between the position of an element in the Periodic Table and the electron arrangement in an atom.

5 Know the names of three alkali metals, their common properties and their place in the Periodic Table.

6 Know the names of three halogens, their common properties and their place in the Periodic Table.

7 From the chemistry of known alkali metals and halogens, be able to predict the properties of other alkali metals and halogens.

8 Know that the term 'bonding' is used to describe the joining of atoms together.

9 Be able to explain two types of bonding: ionic and covalent.

10 Know that substances can exist as simple molecules or in giant structures (or macromolecules).

11 Be able to explain how the physical properties of substances depend upon bonding and structure.

12 Be able to predict probable structure and bonding of an unfamiliar substance using given data.

The Periodic Table

Fig. 1 shows the modern Periodic Table which includes all of the known elements. It is based upon the Periodic Table first devised by the Russian chemist Dmitri Mendeleyev in 1869.

The Periodic Table is an arrangement of elements in order of increasing **atomic number** in such a way that elements with similar properties are placed in the same vertical column or **group**. The horizontal rows are called **periods**.

The shaded elements in Fig. 1 make up the main block of elements. This consists of eight **groups** numbered I to VII.

Elements in Group I are called **alkali metals**.
Elements in Group II are called **alkaline earth metals**.
Elements in Group VII are called **halogens**.
Elements in Group O are called **noble gases**.

The elements between the two parts of the main block of the Periodic Table are called **transition metals**.

In any *period* there is a change across the period from left to right, from metal to non-metal. In any *group* there is an increase in the metallic properties down the group.

The dark, stepped line in Fig. 1 divides the metals on the left-hand

Fig. 1 The Periodic Table

The table is organised into Groups I–VII and 0, with the Transition Elements between Groups II and III. Periods are numbered 1–4 on the left.

Group	I	II	Transition Elements										III	IV	V	VI	VII	0
1	H (1) Hydrogen 1																	He (4) Helium 2
2	Li 7 Lithium 3	Be 9 Beryllium 4											B 11 Boron 5	C 12 Carbon 6	N 14 Nitrogen 7	O 16 Oxygen 8	F 19 Fluorine 9	Ne 20 Neon 10
3	Na 23 Sodium 11	Mg 24 Magnesium 12											Al 27 Aluminium 13	Si 28 Silicon 14	P 31 Phosphorus 15	S 32 Sulphur 16	Cl 35.5 Chlorine 17	Ar 40 Argon 18
4	K 39 Potassium 19	Ca 40 Calcium 20	Sc 45 Scandium 21	Ti 48 Titanium 22	V 51 Vanadium 23	Cr 52 Chromium 24	Mn 55 Manganese 25	Fe 56 Iron 26	Co 59 Cobalt 27	Ni 59 Nickel 28	Cu 64 Copper 29	Zn 65 Zinc 30	Ga 70 Gallium 31	Ge 73 Germanium 32	As 75 Arsenic 33	Se 79 Selenium 34	Br 80 Bromine 35	Kr 84 Krypton 36
	Rb 85.5 Rubidium 37	Sr 88 Strontium 38	Y 89 Yttrium 39	Zr 91 Zirconium 40	Nb 93 Niobium 41	Mo 96 Molybdenum 42	Tc 98 Technetium 43	Ru 101 Ruthenium 44	Rh 103 Rhodium 45	Pd 106 Palladium 46	Ag 108 Silver 47	Cd 112 Cadmium 48	In 115 Indium 49	Sn 119 Tin 50	Sb 122 Antimony 51	Te 128 Tellurium 52	I 127 Iodine 53	Xe 131 Xenon 54
	Cs 133 Caesium 55	Ba 137 Barium 56	La 139 Lanthanum 57	Hf 178.5 Hafnium 72	Ta 181 Tantalum 73	W 184 Tungsten 74	Re 186 Rhenium 75	Os 190 Osmium 76	Ir 192 Iridium 77	Pt 195 Platinum 78	Au 197 Gold 79	Hg 201 Mercury 80	Tl 204 Thallium 81	Pb 207 Lead 82	Bi 209 Bismuth 83	Po 210 Polonium 84	At 210 Astatine 85	Rn 222 Radon 86
	Fr 223 Francium 87	Ra 226 Radium 88	Ac 227 Actinium 89															

Lanthanide series:

La 139 Lanthanum 57	Ce 140 Cerium 58	Pr 141 Praseodymium 59	Nd 144 Neodymium 60	Pm 147 Promethium 61	Sm 150 Samarium 62	Eu 152 Europium 63	Gd 157 Gadolinium 64	Tb 159 Terbium 65	Dy 162.5 Dysprosium 66	Ho 165 Holmium 67	Er 167 Erbium 68	Tm 169 Thulium 69	Yb 173 Ytterbium 70	Lu 175 Lutetium 71

Actinide series:

Ac 227 Actinium 89	Th 232 Thorium 90	Pa 231 Protactinium 91	U 238 Uranium 92	Np 237 Neptunium 93	Pu 242 Plutonium 94	Am 243 Americium 95	Cm 247 Curium 96	Bk 247 Berkelium 97	Cf 251 Californium 98	Es 254 Einsteinium 99	Fm 253 Fermium 100	Md 256 Mendelevium 101	No 254 Nobelium 102	Lw 257 Lawrencium 103

Key

Atomic Mass
Symbol
Name
Atomic Number

side of it from the non-metals on the right-hand side of it. Gases are near the top of the Periodic Table on the right-hand side.

The position of an element in the Periodic Table is related to the electron arrangement in atoms of the element.

Element	Electron arrangement	Group in Periodic Table
Lithium	2,1	I
Beryllium	2,2	II
Boron	2,3	III
Carbon	2,4	IV
Nitrogen	2,5	V
Oxygen	2,6	VI
Fluorine	2,7	VII
Neon	2,8	O
Sodium	2,8,1	I
Magnesium	2,8,2	II

Table 1

Notice, looking at Table 1, that the number of electrons in the outer energy level is the same as the number of the group in which the element is placed. Note, however, that elements in group O (called noble gases) do not fit this pattern.

Alkali metals

Table 2 contains information about three elements in Group I of the Periodic Table. We call these elements **alkali metals**. The alkali metals have low melting and boiling points which decrease as atomic number increases. The pattern of densities is less easy to see but all of these three metals are less dense than water.

Alkali metal	Atomic number	Electron arrangement of atom	Melting point (°C)	Boiling point (°C)	Density (g/cm^3)
Lithium, Li	3	2,1	181	1331	0.54
Sodium, Na	11	2,8,1	98	890	0.97
Potassium, K	19	2,8,8,1	63	766	0.86

Table 2

These metals are all very reactive. They are stored under paraffin oil because they react with oxygen and water vapour. They quickly corrode in air. They burn in air or oxygen to form solid alkaline oxides. For example:

sodium + oxygen → sodium oxide
$4Na$ (s) + O_2 (g) → $2Na_2O$ (s)

They all react with cold water to produce an alkaline solution and hydrogen gas.

lithium + water → lithium hydroxide + hydrogen
$2Li$ (s) + $2H_2O$ (l) → $2LiOH$ (aq) + H_2 (g)
sodium + water → sodium hydroxide + hydrogen
$2Na$ (s) + $2H_2O$ (l) → $2NaOH$ (aq) + H_2 (g)
potassium + water → potassium hydroxide + hydrogen
$2K$ (s) + $2H_2O$ (l) → $2KOH$ (aq) + H_2 (g)

There are differences in these reactions. Lithium is less reactive than sodium and sodium is less reactive than potassium. The reactions become more rapid and violent as we use metals lower down Group I. This applies to all reactions and not only reactions with water.

The halogens

Table 3 contains information about three elements in Group VII of the Periodic Table. These elements are called **halogens**.

Halogen	Atomic number	Electron arrangement of atom	Melting point (°C)	Boiling point (°C)	Appearance
Chlorine, Cl	17	2,8,7	−101	−34	green-yellow gas
Bromine, Br	35	2,8,18,7	−7	58	red-brown liquid
Iodine, I	53	2,8,18,18,7	114	183	grey-black solid

Table 3

The melting and boiling points increase with increasing atomic number. The halogen elements are made up from molecules composed of pairs of atoms. We write Cl_2, Br_2 and I_2 to represent these molecules.

Halogen elements react with metals to form solid compounds called salts. Sodium burns in chlorine to form sodium chloride.

sodium + chlorine → sodium chloride
$2Na$(s) + Cl_2 (g) → $2NaCl$(s)

All halogen react with hydrogen. For example:

hydrogen + chlorine → hydrogen chloride
$$H_2(g) + Cl_2(g) \rightarrow 2HCl(g)$$
hydrogen + bromine → hydrogen bromide
$$H_2(g) + Br_2(g) \rightarrow 2HBr(g)$$
hydrogen + iodine ⇌ hydrogen iodide
$$H_2(g) + I_2(g) \rightleftharpoons 2HI(g)$$

There is a difference in the way that these elements react. A mixture of hydrogen and chlorine explodes in sunlight without heating. A mixture of hydrogen and iodine reacts only partially when heated with a catalyst. In all reactions chlorine is more reactive than bromine, and bromine is more reactive than iodine.

The differences in reactivity of the halogens can be seen in **displacement reactions** of halogens. If chlorine is bubbled through a solution of potassium bromide, a reaction takes place forming bromine.

chlorine + potassium bromide → potassium chloride + bromine
$$Cl_2(g) + 2KBr(aq) \rightarrow 2KCl(aq) + Br_2(g)$$

The solution turns red as bromine is produced. The reaction takes place because chlorine is more reactive than bromine. No reaction would take place if iodine were added to potassium chloride because iodine is less reactive than chlorine.

Bonding

Atoms can be joined together or **bonded** in different ways. There are two different kinds of bonding – **ionic** bonding and **covalent** bonding.

Ionic bonding

Ionic bonding involves a metal atom and a non-metal atom (or group of non-metal atoms) joining together. Charged particles called **ions** are formed. A good example of ionic bonding is sodium chloride.

A sodium atom has an electron arrangement of 2,8,1 and a chlorine atom, an electron arrangement of 2,8,7. A sodium atom has one more electron and a chlorine one less electron than a neon atom. Neon is a particularly stable atom and it can be assumed that it has a stable electron arrangement (2,8).

A sodium atom loses an electron to form a positively charged sodium ion.

$$Na \rightarrow Na^+ + e^-$$

A chlorine atom gains an electron to form a negatively-charged chloride ion.

$$Cl + e^- \rightarrow Cl^-$$

The positive and negative ions are held together by strong **electrostatic forces**. Solid sodium chloride consists of a regular arrangement of positive sodium ions and negative chloride ions. This regular arrangement of particles in the solid (Fig. 2) is called a **lattice**.

Fig. 2 A sodium chloride lattice

Magnesium oxide is another example of ionic bonding.

Magnesium atom 2,8,2   Oxygen atom 2,6

This time each magnesium atom loses two electrons and forms a magnesium Mg^{2+} ion. Each oxygen atom gains two electrons and forms an oxide O^{2-} ion. This time the forces of attraction are greater because the ions have 2+ and 2− charges. As a result, magnesium oxide has a higher melting point and is less soluble in water than sodium chloride.

Covalent bonding

Covalent bonding involves a sharing of electrons. The atoms joined together are atoms of non-metals. An example of covalent bonding is the chlorine molecule (Cl_2).

A chlorine atom can be represented as:

$$\overset{\text{xx}}{\underset{\text{xx}}{_x}Cl^x}$$

where each x represents an electron in the outer (third) energy level. Electrons in other energy levels are not involved.

A chlorine atom has one less electron than the noble gas argon. This has a stable electron arrangement of 2,8,8.

In a chlorine molecule, Cl_2, each chlorine atom gives a single electron to form an **electron pair**. This pair of electrons holds the two atoms together and can be represented by —.

The chlorine molecules produced are separate from one another.

$$\overset{xx}{\underset{xx}{^{x}Cl}} \quad ^{x} \quad \overset{xx}{\underset{xx}{Cl^{x}_{x}}} \qquad Cl{-}Cl$$

Other examples of covalent bonding are oxygen, O_2, and nitrogen, N_2, molecules.

$$\overset{xx}{\underset{xx}{O}} \quad ^{xx}_{xx} \quad \overset{xx}{\underset{xx}{O}} \qquad O{=}O$$

$$^{x}_{x}N \quad ^{xx}_{xx} \quad N^{x}_{x} \qquad N{\equiv}N$$

All hydrocarbons and most carbon compounds contain covalent bonding. Methane, CH_4, contains covalent bonding. Each hydrogen atom has a single electron and the carbon atom has four electrons in the outer (second) energy level. One electron from the carbon atom and the electron from a hydrogen atom form a single covalent bond.

$$
\begin{array}{ccc}
& H & \\
& \overset{xx}{C} & \\
H \; ^{x} & C & ^{x} \; H \\
& \overset{xx}{} & \\
& H &
\end{array}
\qquad
\begin{array}{c}
H \\
| \\
H - C - H \\
| \\
H
\end{array}
$$

Table 4 shows examples of covalent bonding.

$$\begin{array}{cc} H & H \\ \overset{xx}{\underset{xx}{C}} & \overset{xx}{\underset{xx}{C}} \\ H \; ^{x} \; C \; ^{x} \; C \; ^{x} \; H \\ H & H \end{array}$$	$$\begin{array}{c} ^{x}O^{x} \\ _{x} \quad _{x} \\ H \qquad H \end{array}$$
$$\begin{array}{c} H \quad H \\ | \quad | \\ H - C - C - H \\ | \quad | \\ H \quad H \end{array}$$ Ethane	$$\begin{array}{c} O \\ \diagup \; \diagdown \\ H \qquad H \end{array}$$ Water
$$H \; ^{x}_{x} \; H$$ $$H{-}H$$ Hydrogen	$$H \; ^{x}_{x} \; \overset{xx}{\underset{xx}{Cl}} \; _{x}$$ $$H{-}Cl$$ Hydrogen chloride

Table 4

Effect of bonding on properties

Substances containing ionic bonding have high melting and boiling points. The strong forces of attraction within the lattice are difficult to break down. The substances usually dissolve in water to form solutions which conduct electricity. They do not dissolve in other solvents, e.g. hexane.

Substances containing covalent bonding are usually liquids or gases. They are usually soluble in solvents such as hexane but insoluble in water. They do not conduct electricity in any state. Some substances containing covalent bonding, however, are solids. They usually contain large molecules called **macromolecules**. Paraffin wax and starch are examples of macromolecules.

Types of structure

Table 5 summarizes the changes when three solids are heated.

	Iodine I_2	Silicon (IV) oxide SiO_2	Sodium chloride NaCl
Type of bonding	covalent	covalent	ionic
Change on heating to 700°C	dark grey crystal melts and boils, forms purple vapour	no change	no change
Structure	molecular	giant structure of atoms	giant structure of ions

Table 5

Iodine is said to have a **molecular structure**. Although there are strong forces between iodine atoms, the forces between the molecules are weak. The structure breaks down on gentle heating. Sodium chloride and silicon(IV) oxide do not change even if heated up to temperatures of 700°C. In both cases the forces between the particles are very strong and not easily broken. These structures are called **giant structures**. There are two types of giant structure:

(a) Made up from atoms, e.g. silicon(IV) oxide.
(b) Made up from ions, e.g. sodium chloride.

On melting, a giant structure of ions produces **free ions** which conduct electricity.

Summary

The **Periodic Table** is an arrangement of the elements in order of increasing **atomic number**. The elements are arranged in such a way that elements with similar properties are in the same vertical **column** or **group**. The horizontal rows are called **periods**.

In a period, there is a change from metal on the left-hand side to non-metal on the right-hand side. In each group there is an increase in metallic properties down each group.

The position of an element in the Periodic Table is related to the **electron arrangement** in atoms of the element.

Lithium, sodium and potassium are **alkali metals**. They are in group I of the Periodic Table. Atoms of all of these elements have one electron in the outer energy level. These metals are very reactive and the reactivity increases down the group.

Chlorine, bromine and iodine are **halogens**. They are in group VII of the Periodic Table. Atoms of all of these elements have seven electrons in the outer energy level. They are reactive non-metals and the reactivity decreases down the group. Displacement reactions are useful for comparing the reactivity of the halogens.

Two ways of joining atoms together (**bonding**) are **ionic** bonding and **covalent** bonding. In ionic bonding, there is a complete transfer of one or more electrons. Metal atoms lose electrons and form positively charged ions. Non-metal atoms gain electrons and form negatively charged ions. Sodium chloride and magnesium oxide are examples of ionic bonding.

In covalent bonding, there is no complete transfer of electrons. There is a sharing of electrons. The shared electrons form **electron pairs** which hold the atoms together. The atoms joined together are usually non-metal atoms. Examples of covalent bonding include chlorine, oxygen, nitrogen and methane.

There is a clear distinction between a **molecular structure** and a **giant structure**. In a molecular structure the forces within the molecules are strong but the forces between the molecules are very weak. The structure breaks down on gentle heating. Giant structures do not break down on gentle heating because the particles, either atoms or ions, are strongly bonded together.

Revision questions

1 Find the element fluorine, F, in the Periodic Table on p. 134. Now answer the questions which follow.

(a) In which group and period of the Periodic Table is fluorine placed?
(b) To what family of elements does fluorine belong?
(c) What is the electron arrangement of a fluorine atom?
(d) Use Table 3 to predict the melting point and boiling point of fluorine.
(e) Write the name and formula of the compound formed when sodium and fluorine react together. What type of bonding would you expect this compound to have?
(f) Write word and symbol equations for the reaction of fluorine with hydrogen. Suggest what you would see when these two elements react.

2 Table 6 summarizes the properties of five substances labelled **V**, **W**, **X**, **Y** and **Z**. (**Note** These are not the chemical symbols for these substances.)

Substance	Melting point (in °C)	Boiling point (in °C)	Electrical conductivity	
			when solid	when molten
V	787	1437	poor	good
W	114	444	poor	poor
X	1063	2970	good	good
Y	−249	−246	poor	poor
Z	2540	4120	poor	poor

Table 6

Which of the substances:
(a) has the lowest melting point?
(b) is a metal?
(c) is composed of a regular arrangement of small molecules?
(d) has an irregular arrangement of small molecules?
(e) has a giant structure of ions?
(f) has a giant structure of atoms?

3 Ammonia, NH_3, is a gas at room temperature and pressure.
(a) Name the two elements combined in ammonia.
(b) What type of bonding is present in ammonia?
(c) Draw a simple diagram to show the arrangement of outer electrons in an ammonia molecule.

Aims of the chapter

After reading this chapter you should:

1 Be able to construct simple word equations from given information.

2 Be able to construct simple symbol equations, from given information, and balance them correctly.

3 Understand state symbols given in equations.

4 Understand the meaning of the terms in the following list and be able to give examples to illustrate each term: combustion; respiration; photosynthesis; oxidation; reduction; displacement reactions; precipitation reactions; reversible reactions.

5 Know that energy changes can accompany chemical reactions.

6 Be able to explain why energy changes are observed in terms of making and breaking of chemical bonds.

7 Be able to predict the effect of changes in: surface area; concentration; temperature; catalysts; and light on rates of chemical reactions.

8 Be able to state one example of an industrial application of each of the factors above.

9 Be able to sketch, plot and interpret qualitatively, graphs involving, for example, quantity of product against time.

10 Be able to derive simple quantitative measurements from graphical data.

11 Be able to explain the conditions under which enzymes operate best and give examples of enzymes in action.

Word equations

Chemical equations are used to summmarize chemical changes. In all equations the starting materials (**reactants**) are on the left-hand side and the new materials produced (**products**) are on the right-hand side.

reactants → products

We often write the summary of a chemical reaction in words and we call this a **word equation**. For example:

hydrogen + oxygen → water

This summarizes the reaction which takes place when a mixture of hydrogen and oxygen are exploded together. The product is water.

You will be expected to construct word equations, either using your scientific knowledge or, more likely, information given in the question.

Example Iron(II) chloride is formed when heated iron reacts with dry hydrogen chloride. The other product is hydrogen. The correct word equation is:

iron + hydrogen chloride → iron(II) chloride + hydrogen

Symbol equations

You will see symbol equations in text books and examination papers. You would only be expected to *write* simple equations but you might be expected to *use* more complicated equations.

These symbols are understood world-wide and are a way of communicating scientific information which does not depend upon language. Russian and Chinese scientists will understand symbols, formulae and equations even if they do not understand English!

Before trying to write a symbol equation, it is necessary to write a word equation. For example, the reaction of magnesium with dilute hydrochloric acid produces magnesium chloride and hydrogen. First, the word equation is written:

magnesium + hydrochloric acid → magnesium chloride + hydrogen

Then the correct symbols have to be put in:

$Mg + HCl \rightarrow MgCl_2 + H_2$

Symbol equations then have to be **balanced** correctly. This means there must be the same number of each type of atom on both sides of the equation. You must not change the formula of any substance. In the equation we are writing, on the left-hand side we have:

   1 magnesium, 1 hydrogen and 1 chlorine.

On the right-hand side we have:

   1 magnesium, 2 hydrogens and 2 chlorines.

To balance the equation we put a 2 in front of the HCl on the left-hand side:

$Mg + 2HCl \rightarrow MgCl_2 + H_2$

We now have one magnesium, two hydrogens and two chlorines on each side and is said to be **balanced**.

State symbols

Additional information is given in symbol equations in the form of **state symbols**:

(s) solid

(l) liquid

(g) gas

(aq) a solution in which water is the solvent. We call this an **aqueous solution**.

In the equation we were writing above, we would write:

$Mg(s) + 2HCl(aq) \rightarrow MgCl_2(aq) + H_2(g)$

Combustion reactions

K

A **combustion reaction** is a reaction in which a substance combines with oxygen and produces energy. When a combustion occurs **oxides** are formed.

Example Burning carbon in oxygen:
carbon + oxygen → carbon dioxide
$$C(s) + O_2(g) \rightarrow CO_2(g)$$

Example Burning magnesium in oxygen:
magnesium + oxygen → magnesium oxide
$$2Mg(s) + O_2(g) \rightarrow 2MgO(s)$$

Example Burning hydrocarbons (i.e. compounds of carbon and hydrogen only). There are different products possible here. If the hydrocarbon(e.g. methane, CH_4) is burned in excess air or oxygen, carbon dioxide and water are produced:

methane + oxygen → carbon dioxide + water
$$CH_4(g) + 2O_2(g) \rightarrow CO_2(g) + 2H_2O(l)$$

However, if the methane is burned in a limited amount of air or oxygen, carbon monoxide and water are produced:

methane + oxygen → carbon monoxide + water
$$2CH_4(g) + 3O_2(g) \rightarrow 2CO(g) + 4H_2O(l)$$

Carbon monoxide is very poisonous because it combines with haemoglobin in the blood forming carboxyhaemoglobin. This prevents oxygen being transported around the body and leads to death. Adequate ventilation is necessary in a room with a gas fire, to avoid carbon monoxide formation.

Respiration

Respiration is very similar to combustion. The fuel is food. This is oxidized in the cells of the body to produce carbon dioxide and water. If the food used is glucose, the word and balanced symbol equations are:

glucose + oxygen → carbon dioxide + water + energy
$$C_6H_{12}O_6(aq) + 6O_2(g) \rightarrow 6CO_2(g) + 6H_2O(l)$$

Photosynthesis

Photosynthesis is the opposite of respiration. Respiration and combustion both use up oxygen. Fortunately, the oxygen used up is replaced by **photosynthesis** in green plants. Green plants take in carbon dioxide through the leaves. In sunlight, using chlorophyll in the leaves, plants produce sugar. The other product is oxygen which escapes into the atmosphere:

energy + carbon dioxide + water → sugar + oxygen
$$6CO_2(g) + 6H_2O(l) \rightarrow C_6H_{12}O_6(aq) + 6O_2(g)$$

Green plants on Earth are essential for keeping the oxygen level in the atmosphere constant. One fifth of the oxygen is produced in the rain forests of South America, which are being steadily reduced in area. Increased levels of carbon dioxide in the atmosphere lead to the Earth warming up slightly. This is called the **greenhouse effect** (p. 15).

Oxidation and reduction

Oxidation takes place when oxygen is added or hydrogen is removed during a chemical reaction. Reduction is the opposite of oxidation, i.e. oxygen is removed or hydrogen is added.

1 *Oxidation*

Magnesium + oxygen → magnesium oxide
$$2Mg(s) \quad + \quad O_2(g) \quad \rightarrow \quad 2MgO(s)$$

Magnesium is oxidised – oxygen is added.

2 *Reduction*

Ethene + hydrogen → ethane
$$C_2H_4(g) + \quad H_2(g) \quad \rightarrow C_2H_6(g)$$

Ethene is reduced – hydrogen is added.

Very often oxidation and reduction take place together. A reaction in which oxidation and reduction take place is called a **redox** reaction.

Example Lead(II) oxide heated in a stream of dry hydrogen

Lead(II) oxide + hydrogen → lead + water
$$PbO(s) \quad + \quad H_2(g) \quad \rightarrow Pb(s) + H_2O(g)$$

Lead(II) oxide is reduced to lead – oxygen is lost. Hydrogen is oxidized – oxygen is added. Hydrogen, which brings about the reduction of lead(II) oxide, is called the **reducing agent**. Lead(II) oxide, which brings about the oxidation of hydrogen, is called the **oxidizing agent**.

A more complicated definition of oxidation and reduction is: Oxidation is a loss of electrons: reduction is a gain of electrons:

Example $Na^+ + e^- \rightarrow Na$ reduction
$$2Cl^- \rightarrow Cl_2 + 2e^- \quad \text{oxidation}$$

Displacement reactions

Displacement reactions occur between an element and a salt solution. There are two types met commonly:

1 *Metal/metal salt solution*

A metal will replace another metal in a salt solution, provided the metal added is higher in the reactivity series than the metal in the salt (p. 30).

Example Zinc added to copper(II) sulphate solution

zinc + copper(II) sulphate → zinc sulphate + copper
$Zn(s) +$ $CuSO_4(aq)$ → $ZnSO_4(aq)$ + $Cu(s)$

2 *Halogen/halide solutions*
See p. 137.

Precipitation reactions

When some metal salt solutions are mixed together a solid is formed.
This solid is called a **precipitate**.

Example Sodium sulphate solution added to barium chloride solution:

sodium   +   barium   →   barium   +   sodium
sulphate   chloride   sulphate   chloride
$Na_2SO_4(aq) + BaCl_2(aq) → BaSO_4(s) + 2NaCl(aq)$

Reversible reactions

In most reactions the sign → indicates that the reaction goes from left
to right. In some reactions, however, the reverse reaction is *also*
possible. A reaction which can go in the forward and reverse direction
at the same time is called a **reversible reaction**.

Example The Haber process for the manufacture of ammonia:
nitrogen + hydrogen ⇌ ammonia
$N_2(g)$ + $3H_2(g)$ ⇌ $2NH_3(g)$

Energy changes in chemical reactions

In a chemical reaction there is often an energy change which can be
observed. If the reaction *produces* energy the reaction is said to be
exothermic.
Example Mixing solutions of sodium hydroxide and hydrochloric acid:

sodium hydroxide + hydrochloric acid → sodium chloride + water
    $NaOH(aq)$ + $HCl(aq)$ → $NaCl$ (aq)   + $H_2O(l)$

The energy level diagram for the exothermic reaction above is shown
in Fig. 1. The products contain less energy than the reactants. The
surplus energy is given out as heat.
Reactions involving the combustion of fuels are exothermic. A
reaction which *takes in* energy is called an **endothermic** reaction.

Example Mixing together solutions of sodium carbonate and calcium
nitrate:

calcium   +   sodium   →   calcium   +   sodium
nitrate   carbonate   carbonate   nitrate
$Ca(NO_3)_2(aq) + Na_2CO_3(aq) → CaCO_3(s) + 2NaNO_3(aq)$

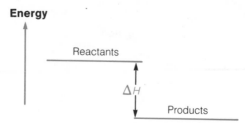

Fig. 1 Energy in an exothermic reaction

The energy level diagram for the endothermic reaction is shown in Fig. 2.

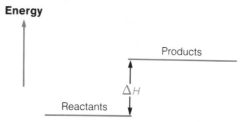

Fig. 2 Energy in an endothermic reaction

The energy taken in or given out during a reaction is called the **heat of reaction** (ΔH). The heat of reaction is *negative* for an exothermic reaction and *positive* for an endothermic reaction. The units are kJ/mol (kilojoules per mole).

Where does this energy come from? During a reaction chemical bonds may be made or broken. Energy is produced when bonds are made and energy is required when bond are broken.

If the energy produced when bonds are formed is greater than the energy required to break the necessary bonds, then the reaction will be exothermic. However, if the energy required to break the bonds is greater the reaction is endothermic.

Factors affecting the rate of reaction

A reaction which takes place quickly is called a **fast** reaction and is finished in a short time. There are a number of ways of speeding up a chemical reaction:

1 *Increasing the surface area of the solid*
Small lumps of a chemical have much larger surface area than a single lump of the same chemical of equal mass. Powders have a very large surface area.

Flour dust in a flour mill has to be carefully controlled. Mixtures of flour dust and air can explode.

2 *Increasing the concentration of reacting substances*
Often doubling the concentration of one of the reacting substances will double the rate of reaction (i.e halve the time taken for the reaction). In reactions involving gases, the concentration can be increased by increasing the pressure.

3 *Increasing the temperature*
The rate of reaction increases considerably when the temperature is increased. A 10 °C temperature rise approximately doubles the rate of reaction.
   The rate of souring of milk or spoiling of food is reduced by cooling. A refrigerator or deep freezer cools the food down and the chemical reactions, which lead to spoiling, are greatly slowed down.

4 *Using a catalyst*
A **catalyst** is a substance which alters the rate of a chemical reaction without being used up. Usually a catalyst is used to speed up reactions.

Example In the contact process to produce sulphuric acid:

sulphur dioxide + oxygen $\rightleftharpoons$ sulphur trioxide
$2SO_2(g)$ $+$ $O_2(g)$ $\rightleftharpoons$ $2SO_3(g)$

The catalyst is vanadium(V) oxide.

Example In the Haber process to produce ammonia:

nitrogen + hydrogen $\rightleftharpoons$ ammonia
$N_2(g)$ $+$ $3H_2(g)$ $\rightleftharpoons$ $2NH_3(g)$

The catalyst is finely divided iron.

   Sometimes a catalyst is used to slow down a reaction. For example, additives are added to food to prevent it from going bad.
   Many chemical reactions taking place in living things are controlled by biological catalysts called **enzymes**. Enzymes are special protein molecules. They have certain specific properties:
1 A particular enzyme will only catalyze certain reactions – not all reactions.
2 They only work over a limited range of temperature, (e.g. enzymes which operate in the human body will work at temperatures around normal body temperature (37 °C)).
3 They will only work within a limited range of temperature.

Examples of enzymes are:
   amylase in saliva which breaks down large starch molecules into smaller glucose molecules

- enzymes in biological washing powders help remove stains, even in cool water
- enzymes in yeast convert sugar into ethanol during fermentation.

5 *Using light*

Some reactions take place faster in stronger light. A photographic film has light-sensitive silver compounds on its surface. When the shutter opens, light enters the camera and hits the coating. Bright light causes more decomposition of the coating. When the film is developed, surplus chemicals are removed from the film to produce a negative.

Studying rates of reaction

Experiments to study rates of reaction always require a stop-watch or stop-clock. Measurements of some kind are usually made at regular intervals, or the time taken until a certain change takes place is measured.

The following examples should show some important principles:

1 *Reactions of lumps of calcium carbonate and powdered calcium carbonate with dilute hydrochloric acid*

calcium carbonate + hydrochloric acid → calcium chloride + water + carbon dioxide

$$CaCO_3(s) + 2HCl(aq) \rightarrow CaCl_2(aq) + H_2O(l) + CO_2(g)$$

A known mass of lumps of calcium carbonate is added to 25 cm³ of dilute hydrochloric acid, as in Fig. 3. Carbon dioxide is produced and the gas is collected in the gas syringe. The volume of gas collected is measured at intervals.

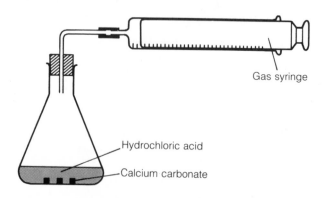

Gas syringe

Hydrochloric acid

Calcium carbonate

Fig. 3 Dilute hydrochloric acid and calcium carbonate

The experiment is repeated with an equal mass of powdered calcium carbonate and a fresh 25 cm^3 sample of dilute hydrochloric acid.

The results of the two experiments are show in the graph in Fig. 4. The reaction with powdered calcium carbonate is much faster. The graph is steeper and the maximum amount of carbon dioxide is produced in a shorter time. When the reaction stops the graph is flat.

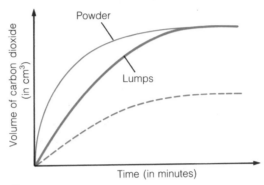

Fig. 4 Graph of the results

The same volume of carbon dioxide is produced in each experiment because equal amounts of chemicals are used.

The dotted line in Fig. 4 shows the graph which would be obtained if half of the mass of calcium carbonate lumps were used with another sample of dilute hydrochloric acid.

The same experiment could be carried out using the apparatus in Fig. 5. This time the reading on the top pan balance is taken at regular intervals. The carbon dioxide escapes from the flask and so the mass of the flask and contents decreases during the experiment. The graph of loss of mass against time is the same shape as before.

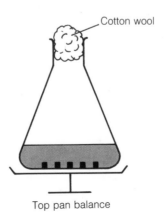

Fig. 5 An alternative method   Top pan balance

2 *Reaction of sodium thiosulphate solution with dilute hydrochloric acid*

| sodium thio-sulphate | + | hydro-chloric acid | → | sodium chloride | + | water | + | sulphur dioxide | + sulphur |

$$Na_2S_2O_3(aq) + 2HCl(aq) \rightarrow 2NaCl(aq) + H_2O(aq) + SO_2(g) + S(s)$$

When colourless solutions of sodium thiosulphate and hydrochloric acid are mixed together, the solution is colourless. However, the solution starts to go cloudy as sulphur is produced. If a cross on a piece of paper under the flask is viewed through the solution, eventually it disappears from view. The time is measured from the mixing of the solutions to the point at which the cross disappears (Fig. 6).

The experiment can be modified to show the effects of changing concentration or temperature.

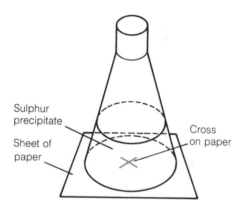

Sulphur precipitate

Sheet of paper

Cross on paper

Fig. 6 Sodium thiosulphate and hydrochloric acid

3 *Decomposition of a solution of hydrogen peroxide*

hydrogen peroxide → water + oxygen
$$2H_2O_2(aq) \rightarrow 2H_2O(l) + O_2(g)$$

The apparatus in Fig. 3 can again be used for this experiment. The experiment is carried out at room temperature without adding any outher substance to 25 cm³ of hydrogen peroxide solution. You will notice no oxygen is produced.

The experiment is repeated with a spatula measure of manganese(IV) oxide added. Oxygen is now produced readily because the manganese(IV) oxide acts as a catalyst.

Hydrogen peroxide is catalyzed by a wide variety of substances including enzymes in blood.

Summary

Chemical reactions can be summarized by **word** or **symbol** equations. Symbol equations must be correctly balanced. **State** symbols in equations give additional information.

Combustion is a reaction of a substance with oxygen, producing **oxides. Respiration** is a similar process which occurs inside our bodies. Food is oxidized to produce carbon dioxide, water and energy. The air we breathe out contains more carbon dioxide and water than the air we breathe in.

Photosynthesis is a process in which plants take in carbon dioxide and evolve oxygen.

A substance which adds oxygen or loses hydrogen is said to be **oxidized**. If oxygen is lost or hydrogen is gained, the substance is **reduced**. A reaction where both oxidation and reduction take place is called a **redox** reaction.

Reactions which produce energy are called **exothermic** reactions and those which take in energy are called **endothermic** reactions. During a reaction, breaking bonds requires energy and forming new bonds gives out energy.

Ways of speeding up a chemical reaction include:
(a) increasing surface area;   (d) using a catalyst;
(b) increasing concentration;   (e) light.
(c) increasing temperature;

Biological catalysts called **enzymes** are specific in their action and work under certain conditions.

Revision questions

1 Use the following information to write word and balanced symbol equations:
(a) Solid iron(III) chloride, $FeCl_3$, is made when heated iron and chlorine react together.
(b) A precipitate of silver chloride, $AgCl$, is formed when solutions of sodium chloride, $NaCl$, and silver nitrate, $AgNO_3$, are mixed. The other product is sodium nitrate, $NaNO_3$.
(c) Complete combustion of butane gas, C_4H_{10}, in oxygen, O_2, produces carbon dioxide and water.
(d) Calcium carbonate is precipitated when carbon dioxide is bubbled through calcium hydroxide solution, $Ca(OH)_2$.
2 An experiment was carried out to measure the volume of hydrogen produced when 1.0 g of zinc chippings (an excess) reacted with 25 cm^3 of dilute sulphuric acid. The results are shown in Table 1.

Time (mins)	0	1	2	3	4	5	6	7	8	9	10
Volume of hydrogen (cm^3)	0	90	160	210	260	300	335	360	380	400	410

Table 1

(a) Draw a labelled diagram of apparatus suitable for carrying out the experiment. (**NB** The volume of gas collected is greater than 100 cm^3 and a gas syringe would not be suitable.)

(b) On the grid in Fig. 7, draw a graph of these results and label the graph A.

(c) The experiment was repeated under the same conditions but with 0.2 g of copper chippings added. The results obtained are shown in Table 2.

Time (mins)	0	1	2	3	4	5	6	7	8	9	10
Volume of hydrogen (cm^3)	0	170	255	320	360	390	420	430	440	440	440

Table 2

(i) Plot these results on the grid in Fig. 7. Draw a graph and label this graph B.

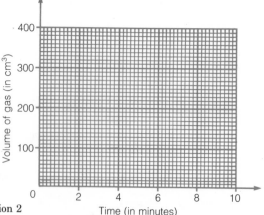

Fig. 7 Graph for question 2

(ii) From graph B, find the volume of gas collected after 2.4 minutes.

(d) What conclusions can you make about the rates of the two reactions at the end of the experiment?

(e) What role is the copper playing in the reaction?

(f) What mass of copper would remain at the end of the experiment?

3 Alkanes are a family of hydrocarbons which fit a formula C_nH_{2n+2}. They burn completely in a plentiful supply of oxygen.

(a) Complete the word equation for the complete combustion of the simplest alkane, methane, CH_4.

methane + oxygen → .... + ...

(b) (i) Complete the energy level diagram for the burning of methane in Fig. 8 by inserting the words *reactants* and *products* in the boxes.
(ii) What chemical term is used to describe reactions which give out heat energy?
(c) The graph in Fig. 9 shows the heat produced when one mole of some alkanes are completely burned in oxygen.
(i) How much heat is given out when one mole of methane burns?
(ii) What is the formula of the alkane containing five carbon atoms?
(iii) Estimate the heat given out when the alkane with five carbon atoms is burned.

Fig. 8 Diagram for question 3

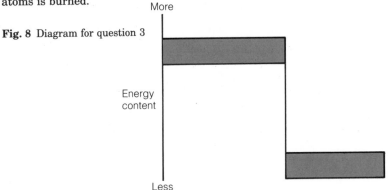

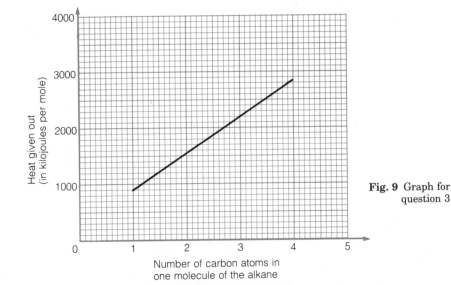

Fig. 9 Graph for question 3

14 Acids, alkalis and salts

Aims of the chapter

After reading this chapter you should:

1 Be able to explain the meanings of the terms *acid, base, alkali* and *salt*.

2 Be able to outline the stages in the manufacture of one mineral acid – sulphuric acid.

3 Know everyday examples of acids and alkalis.

4 Know the names and chemical formulae of common acids and alkalis.

5 Be able to explain the meaning of the term *neutralization* and gives examples of neutralization in everyday life.

6 Be able to recognize substances as acids by their effects on indicators, magnesium and sodium carbonate.

7 Be able to use the pH scale as a measure of acidity and alkalinity.

8 Be able to describe how soluble salts can be prepared by suitably chosen reactions of mineral acids given suitable data.

9 Be able to describe how insoluble salts can be prepared by precipitation, given suitable data.

10 Know the simple chemical tests for metal ions – giving coloured flame tests – carbonates, sulphates and chlorides.

Acids

There are many everyday substances which contain acids. You can recognize an acid by its sour taste.

Examples

Vinegar	ethanoic (or acetic) acid
Fruit juice	citric acid
Soda water	carbonic acid
Apples	malic acid

There are three common acids used in the laboratory. They are:

sulphuric acid	H_2SO_4
hydrochloric acid	HCl
nitric acid	HNO_3

These acids are called **mineral acids**. They are made in large quantities in industry.

Sulphuric acid is the most important acid and is manufactured in very large quantities by the contact process. The process is in three stages.

Stage 1
Sulphur is usually imported as liquid sulphur from countries such as Poland. The sulphur is burned in air to produce sulphur dioxide.

sulphur + oxygen → sulphur dioxide
$$S\ (l)\ \ +\ O_2\ (g) \rightarrow\ \ \ \ SO_2\ (g)$$

The sulphur dioxide is purified. The imputities, especially arsenic compounds, are removed as they can **poison** the catalyst in the next stage.

Stage 2
This step is most important because it is reversible. Unless a good conversion is obtained in this stage, a good yield of sulphuric acid will not be obtained. Sulphur dioxide and oxygen are passed over a heated vanadium(V) oxide catalyst at about 450 °C.

sulphur dioxide + oxygen ⇌ sulphur trioxide
$$2SO_2(g)\ \ \ \ +\ O_2(g)\ \rightleftharpoons\ \ \ \ 2SO_3(g)$$

Stage 3
The sulphur trioxide formed is absorbed in concentrated sulphuric acid forming oleum. Dilution with the correct amount of water produces concentrated sulphuric acid.

sulphur trioxide + sulphuric acid →   oleum
$$SO_3\ (g)\ \ \ \ +\ \ \ H_2SO_4\ (l)\ \ \rightarrow\ \ H_2S_2O_7\ (l)$$
Oleum   +   water   → sulphuric acid
$$H_2S_2O_7(l)\ \ \ +\ \ \ H_2O(l)\ \ \ \rightarrow\ \ \ 2H_2SO_4(l)$$

Because all of the impurities have been removed during manufacture, the sulphuric acid is very pure.

Sulphuric acid factories are usually sited near the coast because:
1 Sulphur is usually imported.
2 Sulphuric acid is easily exported.
3 Any sulphur dioxide which might escape disperses over the sea.

Recognizing acids

There are three tests which can be used to show that an acid is present:

1 Testing with indicators
Litmus is a simple indicator used to test for acids. It can be used as a solution or soaked up in paper – **litmus paper**. If litmus is added to an acid, the litmus turns red. If it is added to an alkali, it turns blue.

Acid	**Alkali**
red	blue

Litmus does not show how strong an acid is. Both vinegar and sulphuric acid turn litmus paper red.

Universal indicator is a mixture of indicators. It changes through a number of colours and, from the colour, it is possible to find out how acidic (or how alkaline) a solution is. This is recorded on a pH scale. A pH of 7 means the solution is **neutral**. If the pH is less than 7 the solution is acidic. Table 1 summarizes the colour which corresponds to each pH.

pH	Colour	Acid/alkali/neutral
1		
2		
3	red	
4		acid
5	orange	
6	yellow	
7	green	neutral
8	blue	
9	indigo (blue/purple)	
10		
11	purple	alkali
12		
13		
14		

Table 1

Natural rain water may turn universal indicator orange. From Table 1 it can be concluded that it has a pH of 5. This means it is a weak acid.

2 *Testing with magnesium*

If magnesium is added to an acid solution, bubbles of colourless gas are produced. If a lighted splint is put into the gas, the gas burns with a squeaky pop. The splint goes out. The gas produced is **hydrogen**.

Example

magnesium + sulphuric acid → magnesium sulphate + hydrogen

$$Mg(s) \quad + \quad H_2SO_4(aq) \quad \rightarrow \quad MgSO_4(aq) \quad + \quad H_2(g)$$

3 Testing with sodium carbonate

If sodium carbonate crystals are added to an acid solution, bubbles of colourless gas are produced. The gas puts out a lighted splint and turns limewater milky. The gas is **carbon dioxide**.

Example

| Sodium carbonate | + | sulphuric acid | → | sodium sulphate | + water + | carbon dioxide |

$$Na_2CO_3(s) + H_2SO_4(aq) \rightarrow Na_2SO_4(aq) + H_2O(l) + CO_2(g)$$

Bases and alkalis

Non-metal oxides such as carbon dioxide and sulphur dioxide dissolve in water to form acidic solutions. These oxides are called **acidic oxides**. Metal oxides are **basic oxides**. Calcium oxide, copper(II) oxide and iron(III) oxide are all basic oxides.

Some basic oxides dissolve in water and others do not. Calcium oxide dissolves in water, forming calcium hydroxide which is an **alkali**. Copper(II) oxide and iron(III) oxide do not dissolve in water.

Common alkalis are:
sodium hydroxide, NaOH
potassium hydroxide, KOH
calcium hydroxide, $Ca(OH)_2$

Everyday alkalis include 'milk of magnesia', lime and ammonia solution.

Neutralization

When an alkali is added to an acid, the acidity is slowly destroyed. If exactly equivalent amounts of acid and alkali are mixed together a **neutral** solution is formed. This process is called **neutralization**.

There are many everyday examples of neutralization:

1 Every adult has several hundred cubic centimetres of hydrochloric acid in the gastric juices in the stomach. This is used in the digestion of food (p. 83). Minor problems of indigestion are caused by excess acid in the stomach. This can be corrected by taking antacids such as milk of magnesia (a suspension of magnesium hydroxide) or bicarbonate of soda (sodium hydrogencarbonate).

2 Lime mortar consists of a mixture of calcium hydroxide and water. This hardens when it absorbs carbon dioxide from the air. The carbon hydroxide is neutralized by acid gases in the air. Calcium carbonate is formed.

| calcium hydroxide | + | carbon dioxide | → | calcium carbonate | + | water |
| $Ca(OH)_2(s)$ | + | $CO_2(g)$ | → | $CaCO_3(s)$ | + | $H_2O(l)$ |

3 Insect bites and stings involve the injection of small amounts of acid or alkali into the skin. This causes irritation. Nettle stings, ant bites and bee stings involve the injection of an acid. The sting or bite should be treated with calamine lotion (a suspension of zinc carbonate) or bicarbonate of soda to neutralize the acidity and remove the irritation.

4 Many inland lakes in Scotland and Scandinavia are becoming increasingly acidic because of air pollution and acid rain. Fish are dying and lakes are becoming totally lifeless. In an attempt to correct this, the land around the lakes is being treated with lime. When the lime is washed into the lakes it neutralizes some of the acidity.
5 Farmers have to control the pH of their soil. If the soil becomes too acidic, a good yield of crops cannot be obtained. Rain and artifical fertilizers tend to make the soil more acidic. The farmer can neutralize land by treating it with lime.

Salts

All acids contain the element hydrogen, which can be replaced by a metal or an ammonium ion. The substance formed when the hydrogen in an acid is replaced is called a **salt** (see Table 2).

Acid	Salt
hydrochloric acid HCl	sodium chloride NaCl
sulphuric acid H_2SO_4	sodium sulphate Na_2SO_4
nitric acid HNO_3	sodium nitrate $NaNO_3$

Table 2

Preparation of soluble salts

A soluble salt can be prepared using one of the following reactions:

$$\text{metal} + \text{acid} \rightarrow \text{salt} + \text{hydrogen}$$
$$\text{metal oxide} + \text{acid} \rightarrow \text{salt} + \text{water}$$
$$\text{metal hydroxide} + \text{acid} \rightarrow \text{salt} + \text{water}$$
$$\text{metal carbonate} + \text{acid} \rightarrow \text{salt} + \text{water} + \text{carbon dioxide}$$

Also:
- If you are making sulphates you use sulphuric acid.
- If you are making nitrates you use nitric acid.
- If you are making chlorides you use hydrochloric acid.

Examples

zinc   + hydrochloric acid $\rightarrow$ zinc chloride + hydrogen
$$\text{Zn (s)} + \quad \text{2HCl (aq)} \quad \rightarrow \quad \text{ZnCl}_2 \text{ (aq)} \; + \; \text{H}_2 \text{ (g)}$$

copper (II) oxide + sulphuric acid $\rightarrow$ copper (II) sulphate +   water
$$\text{CuO (s)} \quad + \quad \text{H}_2\text{SO}_4 \text{ (aq)} \quad \rightarrow \quad \text{CuSO}_4 \text{ (aq)} \quad + \text{H}_2\text{O (l)}$$

sodium hydroxide + hydrochloric acid → sodium chloride + water
$\quad$ NaOH(aq)$\quad$ +$\quad\quad$ HCl(aq)$\quad\quad$ →$\quad\quad$ NaCl(aq)$\quad$ + H$_2$O(l)

$$\begin{matrix}\text{lead(II)} \\ \text{carbonate}\end{matrix} + \begin{matrix}\text{nitric} \\ \text{acid}\end{matrix} \rightarrow \begin{matrix}\text{lead(II)} \\ \text{nitrate}\end{matrix} + \text{water} + \begin{matrix}\text{carbon} \\ \text{dioxide}\end{matrix}$$

$$PbCO_3 \text{ (s)} + 2HNO_3 \text{ (aq)} \rightarrow Pb(NO_3)_2\text{(aq)} + H_2O\text{(l)} + CO_2 \text{ (g)}$$

The method used is outlined in Fig. 1 and Fig. 2. In Fig. 1 the
substance which reacts with the acid is a solid, for example copper(II)
oxide in the preparation of copper(II) sulphate. In Fig. 2 the substance
reacting with the acid is in solution.

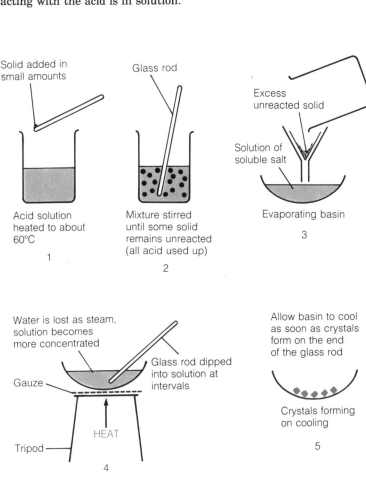

Fig. 1 Preparing a soluble salt (1)

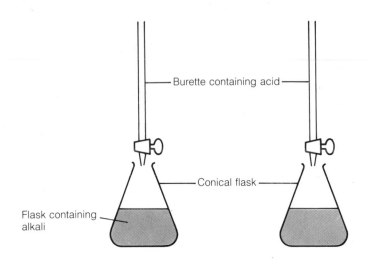

Fig. 2 Preparing a soluble salt (2)

Preparation of insoluble salts

Insoluble salts, e.g. zinc carbonate, are prepared by precipitation (p. 147). Two solutions, one containing a soluble zinc compound and one containing a soluble nitrate, are mixed together. The insoluble salt then precipitates. The precipitate is filtered off, washed with water and dried.

Example

zinc nitrate   + sodium carbonate → zinc carbonate + sodium nitrate

$$Zn(NO_3)_2(aq) + \quad Na_2CO_3(aq) \quad \rightarrow \quad ZnCO_3(s) \quad + \quad 2NaNO_3(aq)$$

Tests for identifying salts

We frequently have to identify particular salts using chemical tests. Here are some of the simple tests that are used:

1 *Metals ions in salts*

Compounds of some metals colour a hot Bunsen burner flame distinctive colours. We can use this fact to identify the presence of some metal ions.

    A little of the compound to be identified is mixed with concentrated hydrochloric acid. A clean platinum wire is dipped into the mixture and the wire is put into a hot flame. Table 3 shows the colours produced by different metal ions.

Ion present	Colour
sodium	orange-yellow
potassium	lilac-pink
calcium	red
barium	green
lead	blue-green

Table 3

2 *Carbonates*

A little of the suspected carbonate is put into a test tube and dilute hydrochloric acid is added. If a carbonate is present the mixture will bubble (**effervesce**). The gas produced turns limewater milky, showing carbon dioxide gas is produced.

3 *Sulphates*

A little of the suspected sulphate is put into a test tube and dissolved in water. Dilute hydrochloric acid is added to the solution in the test tube and finally barium chloride solution is added. A white precipitate of barium sulphate is formed if a sulphate is present.

Example If unknown compound is sodium sulphate:

barium chloride + sodium sulphate → barium sulphate + sodium chloride

4 *Chlorides*

This time a little of the suspected chloride is dissolved in water in a test tube and dilute nitric acid and sliver nitrate solution are added. If a chloride is present, a white precipitate of silver chloride is formed.

Example If the unknown compound is sodium chloride:

silver nitrate + sodium chloride → silver chloride + sodium nitrate

Summary

Acids are compounds of hydrogen and have a sour taste. The common mineral acids are:

sulphuric acid, H_2SO_4
hydrochloric acid, HCl
nitric acid, HNO_3

Sulphuric acid is manufactured in a three-stage process called the **contact process**.

Acids can be recognized by their effects on **indicators**, forming hydrogen with magnesium, and carbon dioxide with sodium carbonate.

The pH of a solution can be found using **universal indicator** or a **pH meter**. A solution with pH of 7 is neutral, pH greater than 7 is alkaline and less than 7 is acidic.

The compounds formed by replacing hydrogen in an acid by a metal are called **salts**. Soluble salts are prepared by the following reactions:

metal + acid → salt + hydrogen
metal oxide + acid → salt + water
metal hydroxide + acid → salt + water
metal carbonate + acid → salt + water + carbon dioxide

Insoluble salts can be prepared by **precipitation**. This involves mixing together two suitable solutions. The insoluble salt precipitates out. It can be separated by filtration.

Revision questions

1 (a) Acidity and alkalinity are measured on the pH scale. Look at the following list of pH values:

pH 1   pH 4   pH 7   pH 10   pH 14

Choose the most likely value for the pH of:
(i)   sodium chloride solution;
(ii) dilute ammonia solution;
(iii) vinegar;
(iv) sodium hydroxide solution.
(b) Some sulphuric acid is dropped onto the laboratory floor. Which of the following chemicals should be put onto the acid *first*?

water, vinegar, sodium hydroxide, sodium hydrogencarbonate.

(c) Which of the warning symbols shown in Fig. 3 should be used on the outside of a container of concentrated sulphuric acid?
2 The label on a brand of antacid tablets gives the following information.

Ingredients:	Calcium carbonate 0.42 g
	Magnesium trisilicate 0.06 g
	Magnesium carbonate 0.06 g
	Sodium hydrogencarbonate 0.06 g

Chew one or two tablets after meals or at bedtime.

(a) What is the acid in the stomach for?
(b) What type of chemical in antacid tablets neutralizes stomach acid?
(c) What is the mass of each tablet?
(d) Suggest an advantage of using the mixture in tablet form rather than as a powder.
(e) What gas is produced when the tablet reacts with stomach acid?

 Oxidizing

 Toxic

 Explosive

 Corrosive

 Highly flammable or flammable flash point below 32°C

 Radioactive

Fig. 3 Warning symbols

(f) What difference does chewing a tablet rather than swallowing it whole make to:
  (i) the speed of action of the antacid.
(ii) the amount of acid neutralized?
3 Table 4 gives information about the solubility of different salts in water.

	Chloride	**Nitrate**	**Sulphate**	**Carbonate**
ammonium	s	vs	s	s
barium	s	vs	i	i
calcium	s	vs	ss	i
copper(II)	s	vs	s	i
lead(II)	ss	s	i	i
magnesium	s	vs	s	i
silver	i	vs	ss	i
sodium	s	s	s	s
potassium	s	vs	s	s
zinc	s	vs	s	i

Key   i=insoluble, ss=lightly soluble, s=soluble, vs=very soluble

Table 4

(a) Using the information in the table, name:
(i) two insoluble sulphates;
(ii) two soluble carbonates;
(iii) two soluble barium compounds;
(iv) one insoluble chloride.
(b) Name the precipitate formed when each of the following pairs of solutions are mixed:
(i) potassium chloride and silver nitrate;
(ii) magnesium sulphate and sodium carbonate;
(iii) sodium chloride and lead(II) nitrate;

15 Metals and polymers

Aims of the chapter

After reading this chapter you should:
1 Know the common physical properties of metals and non-metals.
2 Know common uses of metals and alloys.
3 Know the common chemical properties of metals.
4 Be able to arrange common metals in order of reactivity using simple chemical reactions of metals with air, water or steam and dilute acids.
5 Be able to explain the principles of extraction of metals, relating them to the reactivity series.
6 Be able to explain the extraction of iron and aluminium from named ores.
7 Be able to relate corrosion of metals to the position of the metal in the reactivity series.
8 Know that rusting of iron and steel is a form of corrosion and the conditions necessary for rusting to take place.
9 Be able to explain methods of preventing rusting of iron and steel.
10 Know the meanings of the terms *monomer, polymer, addition polymerization* and *condensation polymerization.*
11 Be able to state examples of natural and synthetic polymers.
12 Be able to describe the formation and use of simple addition polymers such as poly(ethene).

13 Be able to describe the advantages and disadvantages of addition polymers.
14 Be able to explain the differences between thermosetting and thermoplastic polymers.
15 Know some properties of natural polymers such as starch and proteins.

Metals and non-metals

Elements can be divided into metals and non-metals. Metals usually have high melting points. For example, the melting point of iron is 1540 °C. However, mercury is a liquid metal at room temperature and other metals such as sodium and lead have low melting points.

Metals usually have high densities. For example, the density of iron is 7.87 g/cm^3. However, some metals such as sodium and potassium are less dense than water and so they float on water.

Metals are good conductors of heat and electricity. Pure metals are **malleable**, i.e. they can be beaten into thin sheets. They are also **ductile** – they can be drawn into thin wires.

Non-metallic elements can be solid, liquid or gas. They are dull, of low density, brittle and poor conductors of heat and electricity. There are, however many exceptions. Iodine is a shiny solid and carbon (in the form of graphite) is a good conductor of electricity.

There are some elements which are metallic in appearance but are not metals. Silicon, for example, is a grey, shiny solid with a comparatively low density. It is a semi-conductor and is brittle. Elements such as silicon and germanium are called **metalloids**.

The properties mentioned above are called **physical properties**. They are unreliable when used to classify elements into metals and non-metals. If a piece of the element is burned in oxygen, and oxide is formed. The oxide is then tested with universal indicator. This will give the pH of the oxide (see p. 158). If the pH is 7, the oxide is neutral. If the pH is less than 7, the oxide is acidic. If it is above 7, the oxide is alkaline. Metals form oxides that are neutral or alkaline. Non-metals form oxides that are acidic. This is the most reliable way of deciding whether an element is a metal or a non-metal.

Metals and alloys

Pure metals have a number of uses but often the properties of a pure metal are not totally suitable for a particular use. Mixtures of metals, or mixtures of metals with other elements such as carbon added, are called **alloys**. Alloys are widely used in industry and everyday life.

Table 1 shows some uses of common pure metals. Pure metals are usually softer and less strong than alloys. They have higher melting points and are better conductors of electricity.

Metal	Use	A reason for use
Copper	electricity cables	excellent conductor of electricity/very ductile
Tin	coating tin cans	not poisonous
Aluminium	kitchen foil	very malleable
Iron	wrought iron gates	easy to forge and resists corrosion
Lead	flashing on roofs	soft, easy to shape, does not corrode

Table 1

A pure metal is made up of closely-packed positively charged ions held together by a 'sea' of electrons. Fig. 1 shows the arrangement of ions in one layer of a metal. Within the layer each ion is surrounded by six other ions arranged in a regular hexagon. The tight packing and strong forces of attraction between the ions account for the high density and strength of metals. The sea of electrons, which allows electrons to move through the metal, accounts for the electrical conductivity. The malleability and ductility are explained by the ease with which layers can slide over each other.

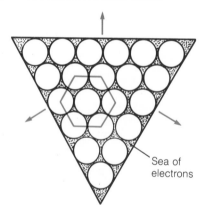

Sea of electrons

Fig. 1 The sea of electrons

When alloys are formed the structure is more complicated, with more than one type of particle present. In a pure metal all of the ions are the same size. In a alloy either ions of different sizes are present (e.g. brass, Fig. 2(a)) or small carbon atoms fit into gaps between the metal ions (e.g. steel, Fig. 2(b)).

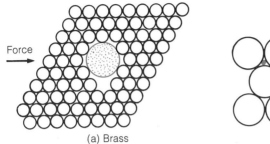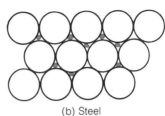

(a) Brass   (b) Steel

Fig. 2 Alloys

Table 2 contains examples of common alloys and their uses. In terms of quantities used steel is by far the most important alloy.

Alloys	Constituent elements	Uses
Steel	iron + between 0.15% and 1.5% carbon. The properties of steel depend on the percentage of carbon. Other metals may be present, e.g. chromium in stainless steel	wide variety of uses including cars, ships, tools, reinforced concrete, tinplate (coated with tin)
Brass	copper and zinc	ornaments, buttons, screws
Duralumin	aluminium, magnesium copper and manganese	lightweight uses (e.g. aircraft, bicycles)
Solder	tin and lead	joining metals (NB importance of low melting point)
Coinage bronze	copper, zinc and tin	1p and 2p coins
Bronze	copper and tin	ornaments

Table 2

Reactions of metallic elements with air or oxygen

Oxygen is a very reactive gas and reacts with most metals. Potassium, sodium, magnesium, aluminium and zinc all burn well to form oxides. For example:

sodium + oxygen → sodium oxide

The metals iron and copper only react slowly with oxygen.

Reactions of metallic elements with water and steam

Potassium, sodium and calcium react with cold water to produce hydrogen.

potassium + water → potassium hydroxide + hydrogen
$2K$ (s)   + $2H_2O(l)$ → $2KOH$ (aq)   + H_2 (g)
sodium + water → sodium hydroxide + hydrogen
$2Na(s)$ + $2H_2O(l)$ → $2NaOH(aq)$ + $H_2(g)$
calcium + water → calcium hydroxide + hydrogen
$Ca(s)$ + $2H_2O(l)$ → $Ca(OH)_2(aq)$ + $H_2(g)$

Magnesium, aluminium and zinc react very slowly or not at all with cold water. The apparatus in Fig. 3 can be used to make magnesium react with steam.

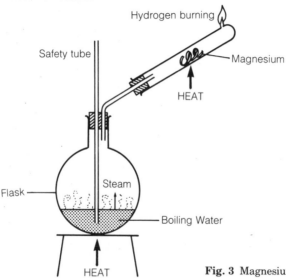

Hydrogen burning

Safety tube

Magnesium

HEAT

Flask

Steam

Boiling Water

HEAT

Fig. 3 Magnesium reacts with steam

magnesium + steam → magnesium oxide + hydrogen
$Mg(s)$ + H_2O (g) → $MgO(s)$ + $H_2(g)$

Iron reacts only partly with steam. Copper and lead do not react with water or steam.

Reactions of metallic elements with dilute acids

Potassium and sodium react violently with dilute hydrochloric and sulphuric acid. Magnesium, aluminium, zinc and iron react with dilute hydrochloric or sulphuric acids. For example:

zinc + sulphuric acid → zinc sulphate + hydrogen
$Zn(s) +$ $H_2SO_4(aq)$ → $ZnSO_4(aq)$ + $H_2(g)$

zinc + hydrochloric acid → zinc chloride + hydrogen
$Zn(s) +$ $2HCl(aq)$ → $ZnCl_2(aq)$ + $H_2(g)$

Copper does not react with dilute hydrochloric or sulphuric acids.

The reactivity series

Table 3 summarizes the reactions of metals with oxygen, water or steam and acids.

Metals in order of reactivity	Reaction with air	Reaction with water	Reaction with dilute hydrochloric acid
Potassium (most reactive)		Reacts violently with cold water to produce hydrogen. Hydrogen burns with a lilac flame.	Violent reaction producing hydrogen. (Dangerous.)
Sodium		Reacts quickly with cold water to produce hydrogen. Hydrogen does not ignite.	
Calcium	Burns in air or oxygen to form an oxide.	Reacts slowly with cold water to produce hydrogen.	
Magnesium		Reacts very slowly with cold water.	
Aluminium		Fairly fast with hot water. Violent with steam.	React with acid to produce a metal chloride and hydrogen. React more slowly down list.
Zinc		Fairly fast with steam.	
Iron		Reacts only reversibly with steam.	
Lead	Converted to the oxide by heating in air or oxygen but they do not burn.	No reaction with water.	Exceedingly slow reaction to produce hydrogen.
Copper			

Table 3

The metals in Table 3 are arranged in order of their reactivity and this is called a **reactivity series**. The series can be extended by adding other metals. Also, it is useful, for some purposes, to include the elements hydrogen and carbon in the reactivity series.

Potassium
Sodium
Magnesium
Aluminium
Zinc
CARBON
Iron
HYDROGEN
Lead
Copper

Displacement reactions

A displacement reaction is a reaction in which one metal replaces another during a chemical reaction (see p. 30). For example, when a mixture of iron(III) oxide and aluminium powder is heated a violent reaction takes place.

iron(III) oxide + aluminium → iron + aluminium oxide
$$Fe_2O_3(s) + 2Al(s) \rightarrow 2Fe(l) + Al_2O_3(s)$$

This reaction is called the **Thermit reaction** and is used to weld lengths of railway track on site.

Extraction of metals

Some of the least reactive metals, e.g. gold, can be found in the form of unreacted metal in the Earth. Other metals can be found as compounds with other unwanted material in the form of **ores**.

The method used to extract a metal from its ore depends upon the position of the metal in the reactivity series. If a metal is high in the reactivity series, its ores are stable and the metal can only be obtained by **electrolysis**. Metals that can only be obtained by electrolysis include potassium, sodium, calcium, magnesium and aluminium.

Metals in the middle of the reactivity series do not form very stable compounds and they can be extracted by **reduction**, often with carbon. Examples of metals extracted by reduction are zinc, iron and lead.

Metals low in the reactivity series, if present in ores, can be extracted simply by heating because the ores are unstable.

We shall consider the extraction of aluminium and iron from their ores in some detail.

Extraction of aluminium by electrolysis

Electrolysis is the splitting up of an **electrolyte** by means of
electricity. The electrolyte may be a molten or an aqueous solution.

Aluminium is found in the ore called **bauxite**. This is hydrated
aluminium oxide, $Al_2O_3.3H_2O$. The ore is purified and pure aluminium
oxide, Al_2O_3, is produced.

Aluminium is extracted by electrolysis of aluminium oxide which is
dissolved in molten cryolite (sodium aluminium fluoride, Na_3AlF_6).
The carbon lining of the cell acts as the **cathode** (negative electrode)
and carbon **anodes** (positive electrodes) are lowered into the cell. Fig.
4 shows a cell used for extracting aluminium.

Aluminium oxide is split up into aluminium (at the cathode) and
oxygen (at the anode).

Cathode $Al^{3+} + 3e^- \rightarrow Al$
Anode $2O^{2-} \rightarrow O_2 + 4e^-$

The anodes burn away in the oxygen produced there and they have
to be regularly replaced.

As this process requires a large amount of electricity, an
inexpensive source, e.g. hydroelectric power, is an advantage.

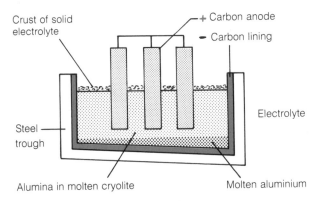

Fig. 4 Extraction of aluminium of electrolysis

Extraction of iron in the blast furnace

Iron is found in a large number of iron ores. One common ore is
haematite ((ironIII) oxide, Fe_2O_3).

Iron is extracted from iron ore, in large quantities, in a **blast
furnace** (Fig. 5). The furnace is loaded with iron ore, coke and
limestone. The furnace is heated by blowing hot air into the base of
the furnace. The temperature of the furnace rises to about 1500 °C. A
series of reactions take place.

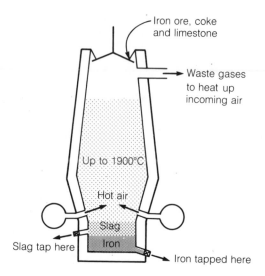

Fig. 5 Extraction of iron in the blast furnace

1 *The burning of coke in the air*

carbon + oxygen → carbon dioxide
$$C(s) + O_2(g) \rightarrow CO_2(g)$$

2 *The reduction of carbon dioxide to carbon monoxide*

carbon dioxide + carbon → carbon monoxide
$$CO_2(g) + C(s) \rightarrow 2CO(g)$$

3 *The reduction of the iron (III) oxide by carbon monoxide – the important step*

iron(III) oxide + carbon monoxide → iron + carbon dioxide
$$Fe_2O_3 (s) + 3CO (g) \rightarrow 2Fe (l) + 3CO_2 (g)$$

4 *The decomposition of limestone produces calcium oxide*

calcium carbonate → calcium oxide + carbon dioxide
$$CaCO_3(s) \rightarrow CaO(s) + CO_2(g)$$

5 *The removal of the impurities as slag*

calcium oxide + silicon dioxide → calcium silicate
$$CaO(s) + SiO_2(s) \rightarrow CaSiO_3(l)$$

The molten iron sinks to the bottom of the furnace and the slag floats on the surface of the molten iron. They can be tapped off separately. The iron coming from the furnace still contains impurities and is called **pig iron**. Most of this is converted into steel.

Corrosion of metals

One of the disadvantages of some metals in use is their tendency to corrode and the costs of preventing this corroding. When a metal corrodes it reacts with oxygen and water in the air. Corrosion is an oxidation process.

There is generally a relationship between the position of a metal in the reactivity series and the way it corrodes. The higher a metal is in the reactivity series the more quickly it will corrode.

Very reactive metals such as potassium and sodium would corrode very quickly. They are stored under paraffin oil to prevent them from coming into contact with air.

Aluminium does not corrode as much as its position in the reactivity series would suggest. This is because there is an insoluble oxide coating formed on the aluminium which prevents further corrosion.

Corrosion of iron and steel is usually called **rusting**. It costs hundreds of millions of pounds each year in Britain. Fig. 6 shows an experiment to find out what causes rusting of iron and steel to take place.

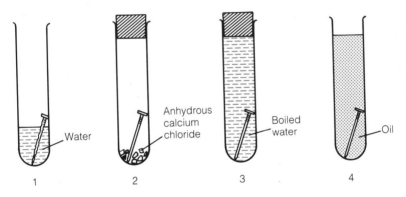

Fig. 6 What causes rusting?

Test tube 1
An iron nail is put into water. The nail is in contact with air and water. Rusting takes place.

Test tube 2
Anhydrous calcium chloride removes all the water vapour from the air. The nail is in contact with air but not water. Rusting does not take place.

Test tube 3
The distilled water is boiled before use to remove any dissolved air. The nail is covered with water. Rusting does not take place.

Test tube 4

The nail is in oil. It is not in contact with air or water. No rusting takes place.

From these experiments, we can conclude that air and water have to be present before rusting of iron and steel can take place. In fact it can be shown that it is the oxygen in the air which is necessary for rusting. Other substances such as carbon dioxide, sulphur dioxide and salt speed up rusting.

Rusting of iron and steel can be reduced by:

1 Oiling or greasing, e.g. keeping the lawnmower blades oiled over the winter.

2 Painting, e.g. iron railings.

3 Coating with plastic, e.g. washing-up racks.

4 Coating with zinc (called **galvanizing**), e.g. metal dustbins.

5 sacrificial protection: if a reactive metal such as magnesium is kept in contact with the iron, the magnesium corrodes instead of the iron.

Although magnesium is expensive, this is a good method for stopping the rusting of a ship.

Polymers

Many of the items which used to be made of metals are now made of plastic materials called **polymers**. A modern car, for example, contains many components made from polymers.

There are many polymers which exist in nature, e.g. cellulose, starch, proteins. They are called **natural polymers**. Probably more important to us today in manufacturing items are the factory-made polymers produced mainly in the last 50 years. They are called **synthetic polymers**. Examples are poly(ethene), polystyrene and nylon. Synthetic polymers are usually made from products obtained from the fractional distillation of petroleum or from coal.

Polymers are made up from very long chain molecules. These long chains are made up by joining together many small molecules called **monomers**. There can be between 1000 and 50 000 monomer molecules linked together in a polymer chain. Fig. 7 summarizes the process taking place during polymerization.

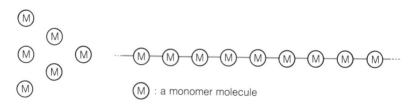

Fig. 7 Polymerization

There are two types of polymerization – **addition** polymerization and **condensation** polymerization.

Addition polymerization
The monomer molecules contain a carbon–carbon double covalent bond. The molecules add together without losing any atoms to form the polymer
$nM \rightarrow (M)n$
An example of addition polymerization is poly(ethene). This is formed by joining together ethene molecules as in Fig. 8.

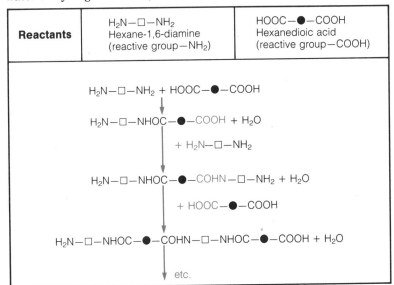

Fig. 8 Addition polymerization

Notice that the polymer does not contain the double bond present in the monomer, ethene.

Condensation polymerization
When the monomer molecules join together, small molecules, e.g. water or hydrogen chloride, are eliminated. The monomer molecules

Reactants	$H_2N-\square-NH_2$ Hexane-1,6-diamine (reactive group$-NH_2$)	HOOC$-\bullet-$COOH Hexanedioic acid (reactive group$-$COOH)

$$H_2N-\square-NH_2 + HOOC-\bullet-COOH$$
$$\downarrow$$
$$H_2N-\square-NHOC-\bullet-COOH + H_2O$$
$$+ H_2N-\square-NH_2$$
$$\downarrow$$
$$H_2N-\square-NHOC-\bullet-COHN-\square-NH_2 + H_2O$$
$$+ HOOC-\bullet-COOH$$
$$\downarrow$$
$$H_2N-\square-NHOC-\bullet-COHN-\square-NHOC-\bullet-COOH + H_2O$$
$$\downarrow \text{ etc.}$$

Fig. 9 Condensation polymerization

must contain two reactive groups. An example is nylon–6,6 which is made by polymerizing two types of monomer molecules: hexane–1,6–diamine and hexanedioic acid (see Fig. 9).
The resulting polymer, nylon–6,6, is a polymer which is widely used for making clothes and home furnishings.

Advantages and disadvantages of addition polymers

Advantages
Addition polymers are usually soft, have low densities and low melting points. They do not corrode. It is possible to make addition polymers which are hard or have high melting points.

An important advantage of addition polymers is the fact that they can be easily moulded into shape, making the production of complicated items such as petrol tanks and car dashboards easy.

Polymers are very unreactive and resist chemical attack.

Disadvantages
The biggest disadvantage of addition polymers comes from the fact that they do not decompose. If dumped on an open tip they do not rot away. They can be destroyed by burning but this is a waste of valuable resources. Sometimes polymers produce poisonous gases when they burn. Re-cycling polymers is obviously the most economic use of resources.

Thermoplastic or thermosetting polymers?

Polymers can be divided into two classes depending upon how they change on heating.

Thermoplastics
These soften on heating and then turn solid again on cooling. They are, therefore, easily moulded. The chain (Fig. 10) are not linked together. On heating they slip past each other easily but on cooling the extra energy is removed and the weak forces between the chains make the plastic rigid again.

Examples of thermoplastics are poly(ethene), polystyrene and nylon.

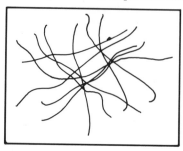

Fig. 10 Thermoplastics

Thermosetting plastics

These can only be heated and moulded once. After forming, they do not melt on heating. On strong heating they may decompose. The chains in a thermosetting plastic are linked together by cross-links (Fig. 11). These cross-links are not easily broken and the plastic will not melt.

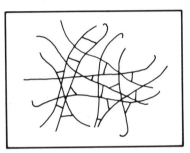

Fig. 11 Thermosetting plastics

Examples of thermosetting plastics are bakelite and epoxy-resin.

Natural polymers

Starch

Starch is a natural polymer made in green plants by photosynthesis (p. 145-6). Starch is a carbohydrate made by linking together glucose molecules. Glucose is the monomer.

Starch is broken down in the digestive process (p. 83) by hydrolysis. The enzyme in saliva (**amylase**) breaks down starch to produce a sugar called **maltose**. Acid hydrolysis produces glucose.

Proteins

Proteins are made by joining together monomer molecules called **amino acids**. There are about 20 amino acids which join together to form proteins. The links between amino acids are called **peptide links**.

Summary

Table 4 compares the physical properties of metals and non-metals .

Metals	Non-metals
Usually solid at room temperature. Shiny. Often high density. Good conductors of heat and electricity. Can be beaten into thin sheets (malleable) and drawn into wires (ductile).	Solid, liquid or gas at room temperature. Dull. Low density. Poor conductors of heat and electricity. Easily broken when dropped or hit (brittle).

Table 4

Physical properties are not always the best way of judging whether an element is a metal or a non-metal. The best method of deciding is to produce an **oxide** by burning the element in oxygen. The oxide is then tested with **universal indicator**. If the oxide is neutral or alkaline, the element is a metal. If the oxide is acidic, the element is a non-metal.

Pure metals are not as widely used for many purposes as mixtures of metals (or metals and carbon) called **alloys**.

Metals can be arranged in order of **reactivity** by comparing the reactions of metals with oxygen, water (or steam) and dilute acids. The **reactivity series** can be very useful in predicting and understanding reactions.

Most metals occur in the ground as **ores** and they have to be extracted from the ores. Metals high in the reactivity series, e.g. sodium and aluminium, are extracted by **electrolysis**. Metals in the middle of the reactivity series e.g. iron, are extracted by **reduction** with carbon. Metals at the bottom of the reactivity series are either found uncombined or are extracted simply by heating.

Corrosion is an oxidation process. The higher a metal is in the reactivity series the more likely it is to corrode. **Rusting** of iron and steel is the most important example of corrosion. Rusting requires the presence of oxygen and water. There are a number of ways in which rusting can be slowed down.

For many purposes metals are being replaced by polymers – the scientific name for plastics. **Polymerization** is the making of polymer chains by joining together small monomer molecules. There are two types of polymerization – **addition** and **condensation**.

Some polymers occur naturally and some are made synthetically from oil or coal products.

Polymers which can be re-melted are called **thermoplastics**. Those which cannot be re-melted are **thermosetting**.

Revision questions

1 Table 5 gives some information about the reaction of three metals **P**, **Q** and **R** with dilute hydrochloric acid. (**P**, **Q** and **R** are not chemical symbols.)

Metal	Reaction with water	Reaction with dilute hydrochloric acid
P	None	None
Q	Slow reaction producing hydrogen	Steady reaction producing hydrogen
R	None	No reaction when cold. Slow reaction on heating.

Table 5

(a) Arrange the three metals in order of reactivity with the most reactive metal first.

(b) Explain how you could find out how the reactivity of another metal, **S**, compares with **P**, **Q** and **R**.

2 Plastics are polymers which are formed from monomers by polymerization.

(a) Complete Table 6.

Plastic	Name of monomer	Structural formula of the monomer	Structural formula of the polymer
	ethene	$\begin{array}{cc} H & H \\ | & | \\ C = C \\ | & | \\ H & H \end{array}$	$\left(\begin{array}{cc} H & H \\ | & | \\ C - C \\ | & | \\ H & H \end{array} \right)_n$
chloroethene)	chloroethene		
rene ιenylethene)		$\begin{array}{cc} C_6H_5 & H \\ | & | \\ C = C \\ | & | \\ H & H \end{array}$	

(b) There are two types of plastic:

Type 1 These can be repeatedly softened and hardened by repeated heating and cooling.

Type 2 These can only be softened once during manufacture. Afterwards heating does not make the plastic melt.

(i) Name the two types of plastic.

(ii) Give an example of each type of plastic and one use of the plastic you have choosen.

Chapter 1

1 (a) Mechanical (or kinetic) into electrical.
(b) Mechanical (or kinetic) into heat and sometimes sound.
(c) Chemical into heat, mechanical and sound.
(d) Electrical into heat and light.
(e) Chemical into heat and light.
2 **A** Conduction; **B** Convection; **C** Convection; **D** Radiation;
E Conduction.
3 Water is a poor conductor of heat.
4 (a) **Fig. 1** (refer to Fig. 21)

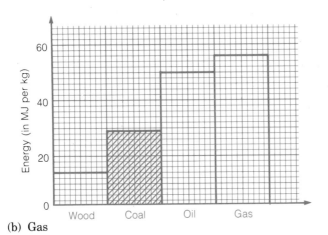

(b) Gas

Chapter 2

1 Electric cooker uses a high current. A separate circuit with a 30 A
fuse protects overloading.
2 (a) Either switch will turn bulb on or off.
(b) Top and bottom of the stairs.
3 (a) BCDE; (b) ACDE; (c) ABDE; (d) ABCE; (e) None.
4 100/240 = 0.42 A   1 A   6p
   200/240 = 0.83 A   1 A or 3 A   12p
   2400 W or 2.4 kW   13 A   £1.44
   12.5 A   13 A   £1.80
5 £57.20
6 (a) X: voltmeter; Y: ammeter.
(b) To adjust the current flowing so different sets of results can be
taken.

(c) **Fig. 2** (refer to Fig. 14)

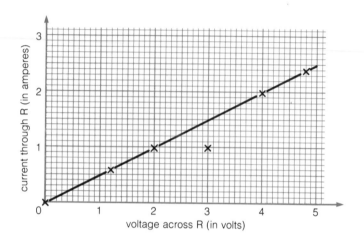

(d) Reading 3 V; 1.0 A.
(e) As voltage increases current increases in direct proportion.

Chapter 3

1 When switch S is opened current in the top circuit is cut off. The solenoid loses magnetism. The armature drops and makes contact in the bottom circuit. Current flows and rings alarm bell.
2 (a) Magnetic field; (b) Repel one another;
(c) Hairspring enables pointer to return to zero when current is cut off.

3 (a) Step down; (b) 40 V

Chapter 4

1 (a) Red and green; (b) Red and blue; (c) Blue and green;
(d) Red, green and blue.
2 Light waves move much faster than sound waves. Looking for the puff of smoke avoids time lag.

Chapter 5

1 Acceleration = $300/100 = 3$ m/s^2;
2 40 mph;
3 (a) $42/7 = 6$ m/s^2; (b) -24 m/s^2;
(c) In a sudden stop by the car, the driver continues to move (called inertia). Unless restrained the driver may hit the windscreen.
4 (a) 1200 N; (b) 120 kg; (c) 200 N

5 (a) The time it takes the driver to apply the brakes.
(b) Directly proportional to the speed of the car.
(c) 12 m;
(d) 9 m;
(e) 20 m/s; $v^2 = 400$, Braking distance = 30 m;
(f) KE = $\frac{1}{2}mv^2$; Braking distance is directly proportional to KE.
(g) Friction between tyres and road is reduced.
(h) KE = $\frac{1}{2}mv^2$ = $\frac{1}{2}m.400 = 200m$
This is converted into PE as the car travels up the ramp.
PE = mgh = $10mh$
All of the KE is converted into PE.
$200m = 10mh$; h = 20 metres.

Chapter 6

1 (a) When temperature rises the bimetallic strip bends and the contacts meet. Current flows and the bell rings.
(b) Bell stops ringing if wires burn through.
(c) **Fig. 3**

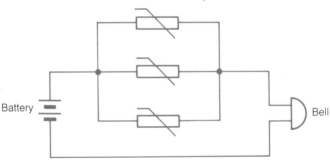

3 thermistors in different sites around the factory

Battery

Bell

2 (a)

Input		Output
S_1	S_2	
0	0	0
0	1	1
1	0	1
1	1	1

(b) OR;   (c) **Fig. 4**

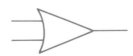

Chapter 7

1 (a) Capillary; (b) Vein; (c) Artery.
2 (a) Brand **X**. Much lower fat and carbohydrate.
(b) Sugar; (c) Chilled cabinet;
(d) Protein 5.0 g; Fat 3.0 g; Carbohydrate 23.0 g.
3 (a) A: artery; B: capillaries; C: vein;
(b) The blood going to the arteries and the blood going to the lungs are kept separate. The right ventricle pumps blood to the lungs and the left ventricle pumps blood to the body.
(c) (i) Exercise increases the efficiency of the heart in pumping blood around the body. A low fat diet reduces the risk of cholesterol building up and blocking the arteries.
(ii) Heavy smokers are more likely to die of heart disease. Smoking reduces the oxygen-carrying capacity of the blood. The heart has to work harder as a pump, making a heart attack more likely.

Chapter 8

1 (a) Red; **R** and **r**.   White; **r** and **r**.
(b) **R**: dominant; **r**: recessive.
(c) **Fig. 5**

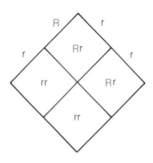

(d) 50 red and 50 white.
2 Dark-coloured moths would not be seen, light-coloured moths would. Predators would eat light-coloured mtohs. Dark-coloured moths predominate.
3 (a) Hover-fly; (b) Number of pairs of wings;
(c) (i) Predator unable to distinguish honey-bee and hover-fly. Knows from experience that honey-bee stings. Not prepared to take the chance;
(ii) Hover-flies with genes giving yellow/black striping are advantaged and breed successfully.

Chapter 9

1 Motorway verges are an undisturbed environment. Growth of
numbers of all species including mice, voles etc. They provide a good
source of food for kestrels.
2 (a) Numbers of frogs, hedgehogs, stoats could rise.
(b) Competition for alternative sources of food could affect numbers of
owls and stoats.

3 Population $= \dfrac{50 \times 20}{4} = 250$

4 (a) Aphids;   (b) **Fig. 6** (refer to Fig. 9)

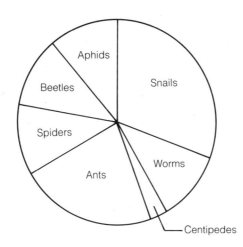

(c) Centipedes — fewer numbers. Therefore, higher up the pyramid of
numbers.

Chapter 10

1 (a) (i) Mercury; (ii) Mercury and Venus; (iii) Earth; (iv) Jupiter;
(b) Mercury, Venus, Earth, Mars, Jupiter, Saturn, Uranus, Neptune,
Pluto;
(c) Planets close to the Sun have smaller diameters and larger
densities than planets furthest from the Sun.
2 (a) Earthquake activity along edges of plates.
(b) Earthquakes occur when moving plates rub against each other.

Chapter 11

1 (a) Ether evaporates away.
(b) Evaporation removes heat energy. Water under beaker freezes.
(c) Diffusion.

2 **Fig. 7** Arrangement of p, n and e in various atoms

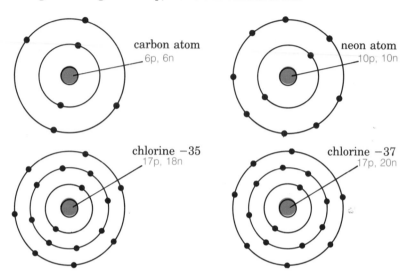

carbon atom
6p, 6n

neon atom
10p, 10n

chlorine −35
17p, 18n

chlorine −37
17p, 20n

3 (a) **Fig. 8** (refer to Fig. 17)

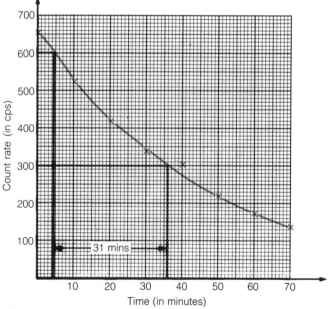

31 mins

Count rate (in cps)

Time (in minutes)

(b) 40 mins; (c) 380 ± 10 cps; (d) 31 ± 1 minutes

Chapter 12

1 (a) VII; (b) Halogens; (c) 2,7;
(d) Approximate melting point -200 to -240 °C; approximate boiling
point -180 to -190 °C.
(e) NaF – ionic;
(f) Hydrogen + fluorine → hydrogen fluorine
      $H_2(g)$ + $F_2(g)$ → $2HF(g)$
Explosion.
2 (a) Y; (b) X; (c) W; (d) Y; (e) V; (f) Z.
3 (a) Nitrogen and hydrogen; (b) Covalent.
(c) **Fig. 9**

$$H \overset{xx}{\underset{x\bullet}{\overset{x}{\bullet}}} N \overset{x}{\bullet} H$$

Chapter 13

1 (a)   Iron + chlorine → iron(III) chloride
      $2Fe(s) + 3Cl_2(g)$ → $2FeCl_3(s)$
(b)   silver + sodium → silver + sodium
      nitrate   chloride   chloride   nitrate
   $AgNO_3(aq) + NaCl(aq)$ → $AgCl(s) + NaNO_3(aq)$
(c)   Butane + oxygen → carbon dioxide + water
   $2C_4H_{10}(g) + 13O_2(g)$ → $8CO_2(g)$ + $10H_2O(l)$
(d) Calcium hydroxide + carbon dioxide → calcium carbonate + water
      $Ca(OH)_2(aq)$ + $CO_2(g)$ → $CaCO_3(s)$ + $H_2O(l)$
2 (a) Collect gas over water using a large measuring cylinder.
(b) **Fig. 10** (refer to Fig. 7)

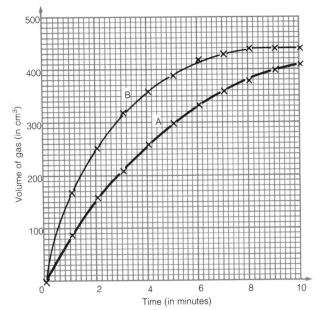

(c) See graph above.
(d) Reaction with copper present is faster.
(e) Catalyst. (f) 0.2 g.
3 (a) Carbon dioxide and water;
(b) (i) Top box −reactants; Bottom box− products;
(ii) Exothermic;
(c) (i) 1000 kJ;
(ii) C_5H_{12};
(iii) 3600 kJ per mole.

Chapter 14

1 (a) (i) pH 7; (ii) pH 10; (iii) pH 4; (iv) pH 14;
(b) Sodium hydrogencarbonate; (c) Toxic, corrosive, oxidizing.
2 (a) Digesting food; (b) Alkali; (c) 0.60 g; (d) Each tablet contains a
measured dose; (e) Carbon dioxide; (f) (i) faster-larger surface area;
(ii) same −same amount of chemicals.
3 (a) (i) Barium sulphate, lead(II) sulphate;
(ii) Sodium carbonate, potassium carbonate, ammonium carbonate
(any two);
(iii) Barium chloride, barium nitrate;
(iv) Silver chloride;
(b) (i) Silver chloride; (ii) Magnesium carbonate;
(iii) Lead(II) chloride.

Chapter 15

1 (a) **QPR**;
(b) Attempt reactions of **S** with water and dilute hydrochloric acid.
Then try to carry out displacement reactions by adding pieces of metal
S to solutions of salts of **P, Q** and **R**.
2 (a) Poly(ethene)
Fig. 11
(refer to Table 6)

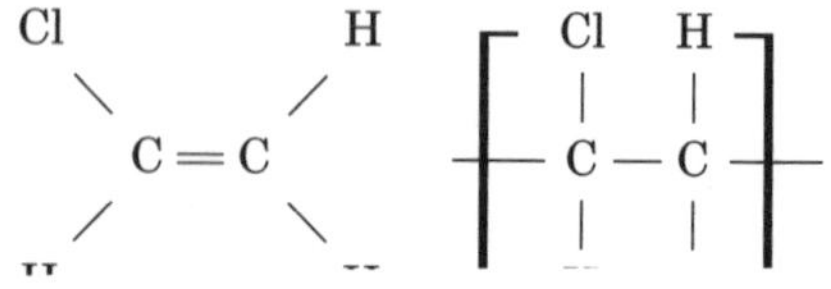

Cl   H   Cl   H

C = C   C − C

Styrene or phenylethene:

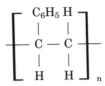

(b) (i) Type 1 −thermoplastic; Type 2 − thermosetting;
(ii) e.g. poly(ethene) −packaging material, milk crates;
e.g. Bakelite — light switches and plugs.

Having followed a planned revision programme, you should be well prepared for the examinations. You should be confident about your chances of success.

On some papers you will not be expected to write essays to answer questions. You may meet different kinds of questions.

1 *Short answer questions*

The answers may be a word, phrase or possibly a sentence. You may also be expected to complete a table or a diagram.

2 *Structured questions*

These are a series of questions about the same situation. Often the questions start easily but get more difficult.

3 *Multiple choice questions*

These questions are less common than they used to be. They consist of a question (called the stem) and five alternative answers. You have to select the correct answer (called the key) from the incorrect answers (called the distractors).

Example What colour is hydrated copper(II) sulphate?

A white   B blue   C green   D black   E yellow

Correct answer–B

The following advice may help you achieve your best:

1 Make sure you have a good night's sleep before the examination. Do not become over-tired.

2 Make sure you have all the equipment you need ready the night before–pen, pencil, ruler and calculator.

3 Arrive in good time for the examination.

4 Make sure you know the length of the paper and number of questions you must attempt.

5 Do not waste time trying to answer questions you cannot do. Leave out these questions and come back to them.

6 Read the questions thoroughly. GCSE questions contain a great deal of information but candidates do not always use it.

7 Write clearly using good English.

8 The number of marks for each question is usually given. This should give you some idea of what is required by the examiner.

9 In calculations, make sure you show the working and units.

10 If you finish the paper early, go back and check your answers.

The GCSE examinations demand a positive response. You must show 'positive achievement' and get higher marks than before. This does not mean it is harder to get a grade C, for example. Unlike GCE and CSE examinations, you are not competing with other candidates. If you can show the examiner that you can meet the assessment objectives, the grade you achieve will reflect this.